ACTION

CONTENTS 2002

ACTION MAN

ANNUAL 2002

Pedigree®

Published by Pedigree Books Limited
The Old Rectory, Matford Lane, Exeter EX2 4PS
E-mail books@pedigreegroup.co.uk
Published in 2001

£6.99

File Edit View Special Diagnostic Keyboard

EDA Internet

www.actionman.com/eda

Back Forward Stop Refresh Home

Address: http://www.actionman.com/eda

ACTION MAN

Mission | Equipment | Reconnaissance | E-Mail | Encoding | Decoding | Keyboard

Mission

Equipment

Reconnaissance

E-Mail

Encoding

Decoding

Keyboard

Incoming E-Mail – Secure Link Decoding

>>Jvsq: Egxmsr Qer (lxxt://aaa.egxmsrqer.gsq) >>Wyfnigx: Qmwwmsr: Qsrwxiv jvsq xli Hiit

Xli rsxifsso csy wii fijsvi csy mw xli THE (Tivwsrep Hmkmxep Ewwmwxerx), xli ribx kirivexmsr sj wstlmwxmgexih gsqtyxivw. Xli THE, zme wexippmxi pmrow, ampp eppsa csy rsx srpc xs oiit mr gpswi gsrxegx amxl qi, irefpmrk csy xs vixvmizi erh wirh qi mqtsvxerx mrjsvqexmsr gvygmep xs qc qmwwmsrw… Mx ampp epws lipt xs csy, xlvsykl qmwwmsr ibivgmwiw, xs figsqi er I

Tviww mgsr ex fsxxsq sj x … syv oic hexe jsv qi xs ythexi

Egxmsr Qer

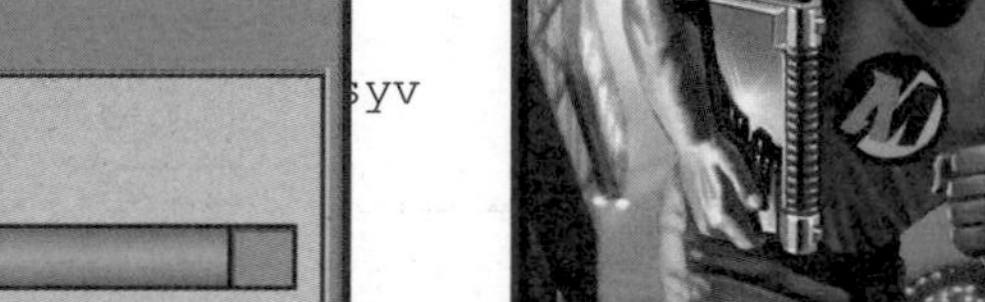

Message as follows

>>*From:* Action Man (http://www.actionman.com) >>*Subject:* Mission: Monster from the Deep

The notebook you see before you is the PDA (Personal Digital Assistant), the next generation of sophisticated computers.

The PDA, via satellite links, will allow you not only to keep in close contact with me, enabling you to retrieve and send me important information crucial to my missions…

It will also help to train you, through mission exercises, to become an EDA (European Defence Agency) top agent yourself!

Press icon at bottom of screen to pull up Personal Data page. Enter all your key data for me to update my files.

Good luck and let's get Xtreme!

Action Man

end transmission

AM2001PDA Specification

Computer: 500Mhz NASA Grade Processor; 256Mb Memory; 18Gb Ultra Fast Hard Disc; TFT flat screen display; Microwave and Infrared data link; Secure satellite up-link; Universal drive (accepts all known types of disc.)

Casing: Matt grey casing with Action Man Tattoo.

Optional disguised version available for undercover EDA operatives.

Ultra Secret - AM2002PDA

File Edit View Special Diagnostic Keyboard — EDA Internet

www.actionman.com/eda

Back Forward Stop Refresh Home

Address: http://www.actionman.com/eda

ACTION MAN

Mission | Equipment | Reconnaissance | E-Mail | Encoding | Decoding | Keyboard

Mission
Equipment
Reconnaissance
E-Mail
Encoding
Decoding
Keyboard

Personal Data Page

Name: Unknown
Code Name: Action Man
Age: 25
Height: 185cm
Distinguishing features: scar on cheek

Specialist Skills — ***Ratings 1-5***

- Weapons
- Martial Arts
- Survival Training
- Pilot/Flying Skills
- Communications
- Computer Skills

Notes: Extreme Sports competitor, highly intelligent and resourceful, fit and strong, high-endurance stamina, computer literate, somewhat reckless, ironic sense of humour. Goal in life: to capture Dr. X and bring down his evil web of allies.

Personal Data Form

Squad Profiles

EDA Undercover Operative – Personal Data
Please enter your personal details into the EDA database

Name ____ *Code Name* ____
Age ____ *Height* ____
Distinguishing Features ____

Specialist Skills — *Rating 1-5*

- Weapons:
- Martial Arts:
- Survival Training:
- Pilot/Flying Skills:
- Communications:
- Navigation:
- Computer Skills:

Notes:

Add EDA Operative photograph here

INITIATE COMMS. MISSION STATUS MIC AM2002PDA

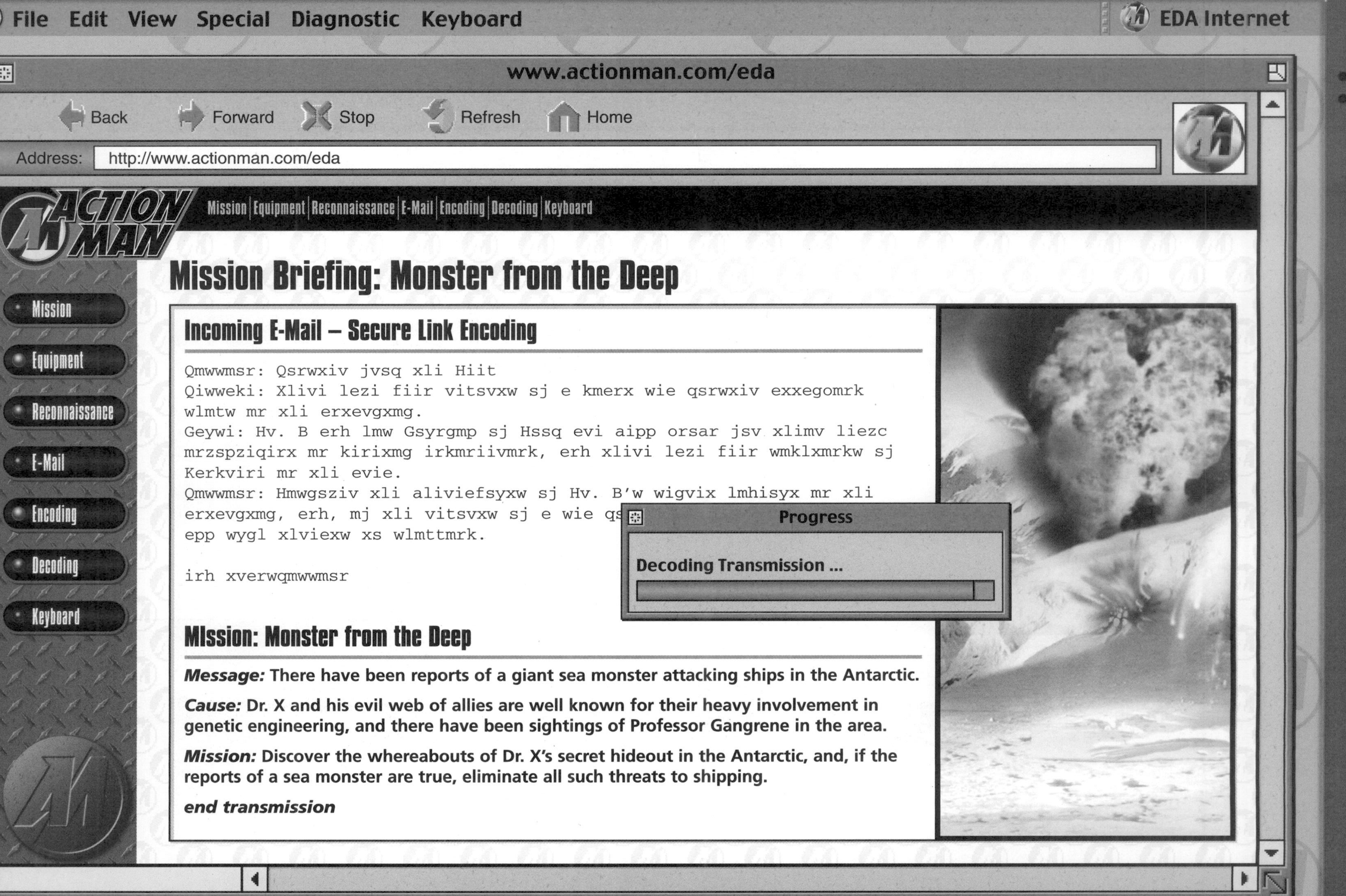
File Edit View Special Diagnostic Keyboard
EDA Internet
www.actionman.com/eda
Back Forward Stop Refresh Home
Address: http://www.actionman.com/eda
ACTION MAN
Mission | Equipment | Reconnaissance | E-Mail | Encoding | Decoding | Keyboard
Mission
Equipment
Reconnaissance
E-Mail
Encoding
Decoding
Keyboard
Mission Briefing: Monster from the Deep
Incoming E-Mail – Secure Link Encoding
Qmwwmsr: Qsrwxiv jvsq xli Hiit
Qiwweki: Xlivi lezi fiir vitsvxw sj e kmerx wie qsrwxiv exxegomrk wlmtw mr xli erxevgxmg.
Geywi: Hv. B erh lmw Gsyrgmp sj Hssq evi aipp orsar jsv xlimv liezc mrzspziqirx mr kirixmg irkmriivmrk, erh xlivi lezi fiir wmklxmrkw sj Kerkviri mr xli evie.
Qmwwmsr: Hmwgsziv xli aliviefsyxw sj Hv. B'w wigvix lmhisyx mr xli erxevgxmg, erh, mj xli vitsvxw sj e wie qs
epp wygl xlviexw xs wlmttmrk.
irh xverwqmwwmsr
Progress
Decoding Transmission ...
Mission: Monster from the Deep
Message: There have been reports of a giant sea monster attacking ships in the Antarctic.
Cause: Dr. X and his evil web of allies are well known for their heavy involvement in genetic engineering, and there have been sightings of Professor Gangrene in the area.
Mission: Discover the whereabouts of Dr. X's secret hideout in the Antarctic, and, if the reports of a sea monster are true, eliminate all such threats to shipping.
end transmission

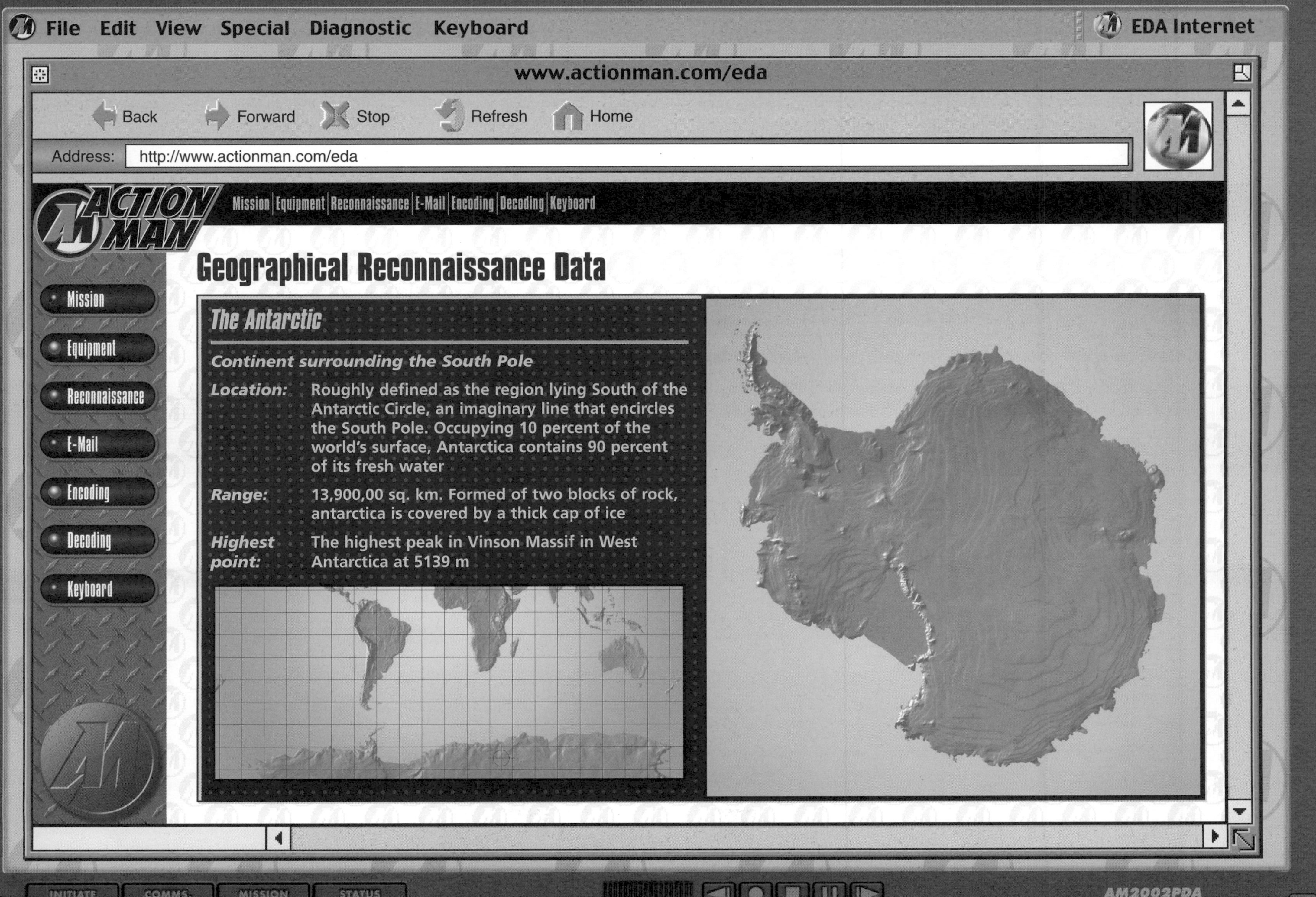
File Edit View Special Diagnostic Keyboard
EDA Internet
www.actionman.com/eda
Back Forward Stop Refresh Home
Address: http://www.actionman.com/eda
ACTION MAN
Mission | Equipment | Reconnaissance | E-Mail | Encoding | Decoding | Keyboard
Geographical Reconnaissance Data
Mission
Equipment
Reconnaissance
E-Mail
Encoding
Decoding
Keyboard
The Antarctic
Continent surrounding the South Pole
Location: Roughly defined as the region lying South of the Antarctic Circle, an imaginary line that encircles the South Pole. Occupying 10 percent of the world's surface, Antarctica contains 90 percent of its fresh water
Range: 13,900,00 sq. km. Formed of two blocks of rock, antarctica is covered by a thick cap of ice
Highest point: The highest peak in Vinson Massif in West Antarctica at 5139 m
INITIATE
COMMS.
MISSION
STATUS
MIC
AM2002PDA

File Edit View Special Diagnostic Keyboard — EDA Internet

www.actionman.com/eda

Back Forward Stop Refresh Home

Address: http://www.actionman.com/eda

ACTION MAN

Mission | Equipment | Reconnaissance | E-Mail | Encoding | Decoding | Keyboard

- Mission
- Equipment
- Reconnaissance
- E-Mail
- Encoding
- Decoding
- Keyboard

Mission Data: Equipment

Arctic Rally Car

Frame:	Carbon fibre bonded to aluminium frame with kevlar armour
EFT:	Epoxy resin fluid-filled all-terrain spiked tyres for gripping the ice
Engine:	Front mounted x15 with twin turbos
Navigation:	GPS (Global Positioning System)
Speed:	0-150 mph in six seconds (ice conditions)
Weapons:	Two multipurpose Sidewinder missiles. Range 2km

In a class of it's own!

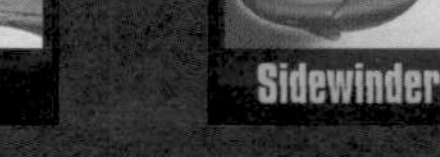

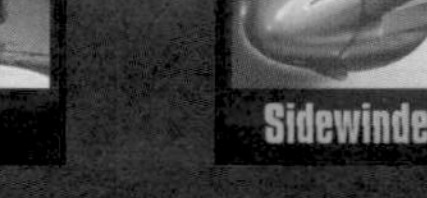

File Edit View Special Diagnostic Keyboard EDA Internet

www.actionman.com/eda

Back Forward Stop Refresh Home

Address: http://www.actionman.com/eda

ACTION MAN

Mission | Equipment | Reconnaissance | E-Mail | Encoding | Decoding | Keyboard

Mission

Equipment

Reconnaissance

E-Mail

Encoding

Decoding

Keyboard

Mission Data: Equipment

Arctic Surf Bike

Frame: Polycarbonate and magnesium composite

EFT: The snowboard base is made from new, tough, lightweight polycarbonate material that is impact resilient

Mobility: Ultra sensitive handling means the ASB can turn sharply at high speeds

Speed: Can reach speeds of up to 90 mph in clear conditions

Weapons: Miniature Sidewinder missile launcher positioned beneath handlebars. Two more missiles attached to snowboard base. Range 1.5 km

Time to chill out!

Composite frame

Snowboard

Sidewinder

INITIATE COMMS. MISSION STATUS

MIC

AM2002PDA

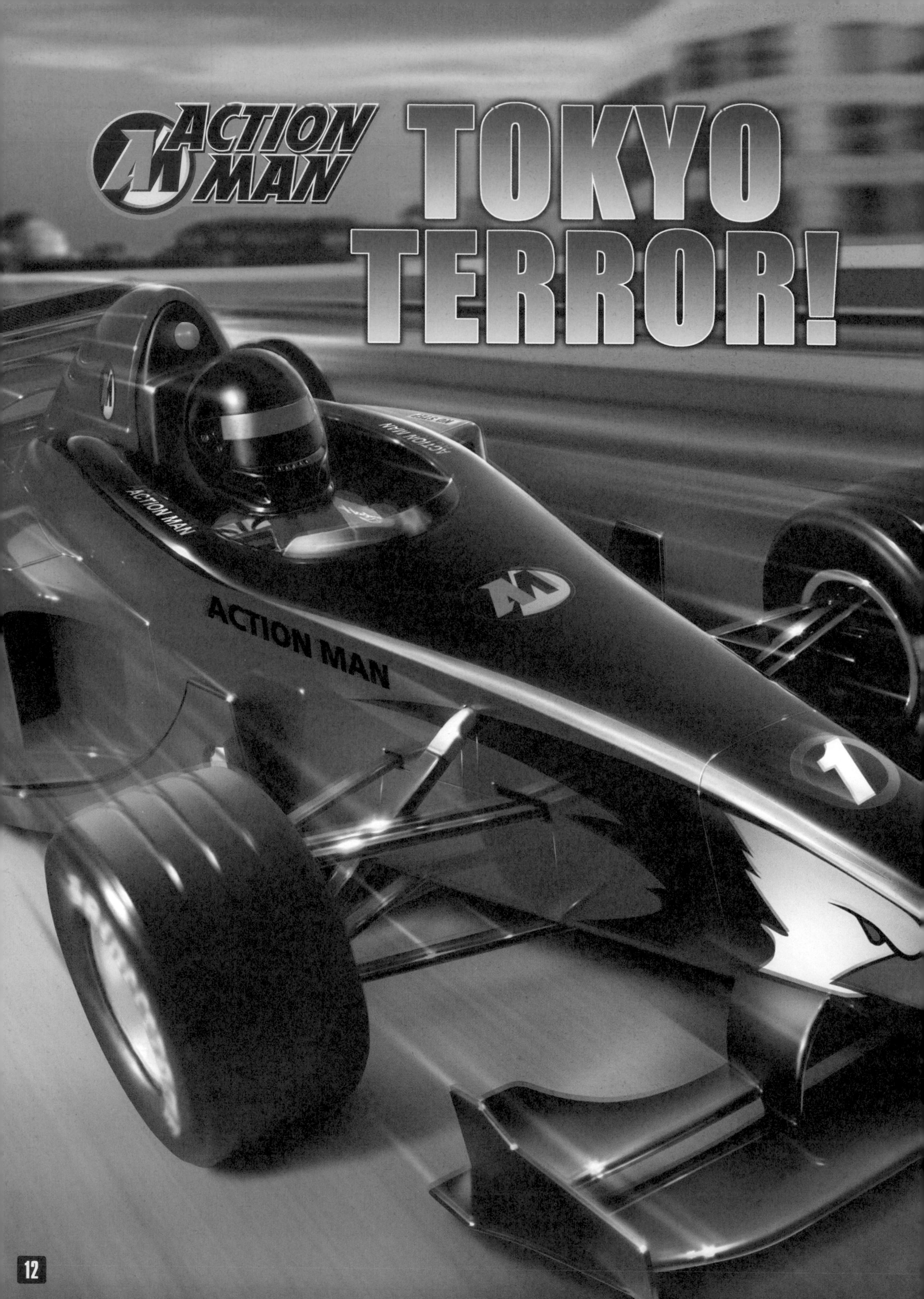
ACTION MAN
TOKYO TERROR!
ACTION MAN
ACTION MAN
ACTION MAN
1

TOKYO, JAPAN. THE STREETS OF THE ARE DESERTED OF TRAFFIC AS THE CITIZENS HEED THE WARNINGS TO STAY INDOORS!
DID WE SAY DESERTED? ALL EXCEPT FOR ACTION MAN, THAT IS!
DR. X IS UP TO HIS USUAL GAMES! HE'S LEAVING CLUES ACROSS THE CITY AS TO THE WHEREABOUTS OF HIS HIDDEN 'X'-TOWERS!
BUT I'VE ONLY GOT ONE HOUR TO FIND THE BUILDING BEFORE THE BOMB EXPLODES, RELEASING THE 'NIGHTMARE' GAS INTO THE ATMOSPHERE!
VROOOMM!
60.00.

AND IT DOESN'T LOOK LIKE HE'S GOING TO MAKE IT EASY ON ME!

VROOOMM!

59.50.

DR. X'S MEN SANDWICH ACTION MAN'S KART EXTREME BETWEEN THEM!

WE'RE GONNA PUT THE ***SQUEEZE*** ON YOU NOW, ACTION MAN!

KRRAANNG!

59.43.

IN FACT, WE'RE GONNA **BLOW** YOU **OUT** FOR GOOD! HA-HA!
WHIRRR!
59.37.
59.31.
SORRY, GUYS, BUT IT'S TIME TO PUT THE **BRAKES** ON YOUR FUN!
SCREEECCCH!
WHAT THE - ?!
PHSSSSSSSSS!
OH, NO! WATCH OUT!
59.30.

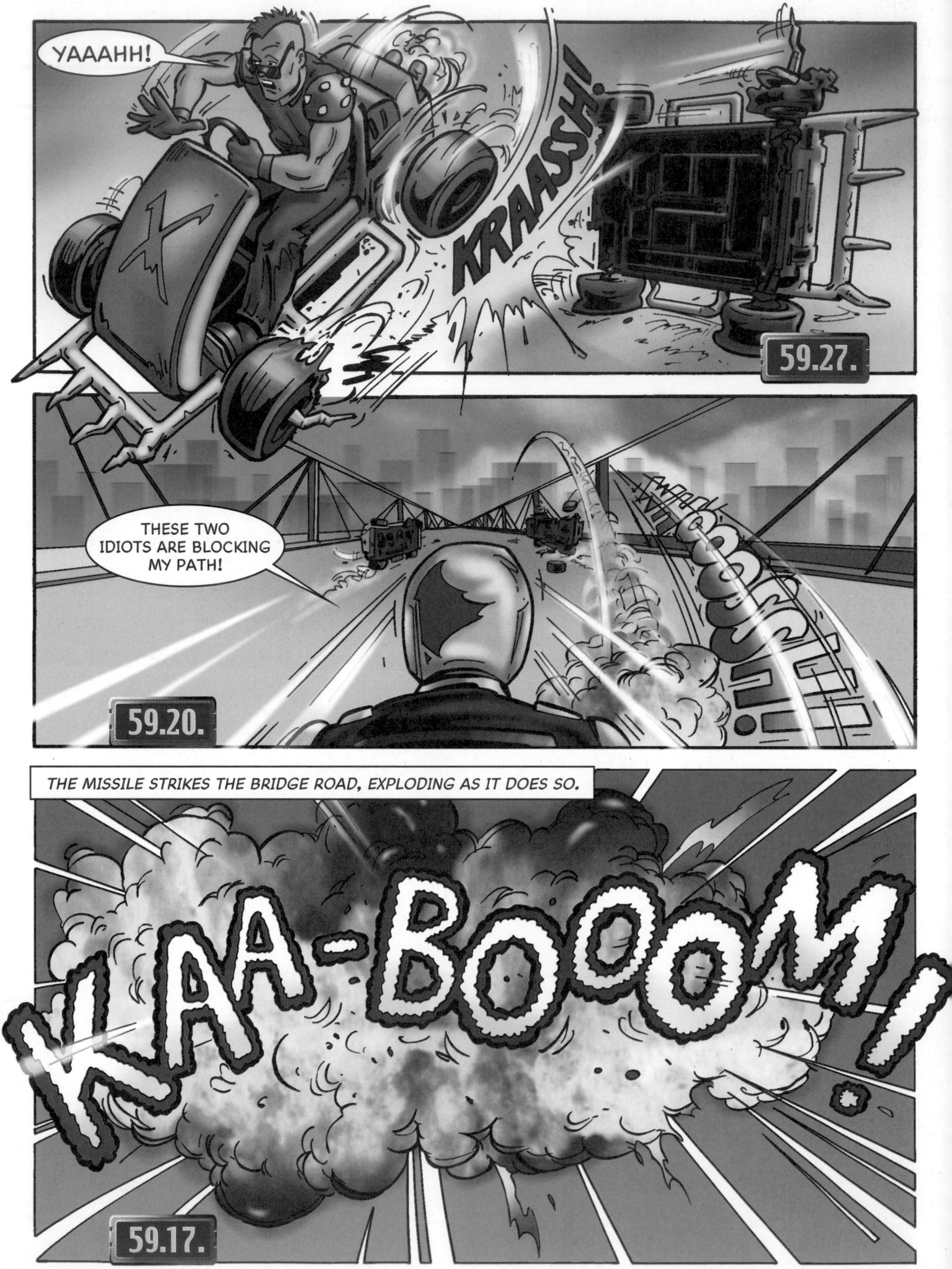

YAAAHH!

KRAASH!

59.27.

THESE TWO IDIOTS ARE BLOCKING MY PATH!

59.20.

THE MISSILE STRIKES THE BRIDGE ROAD, EXPLODING AS IT DOES SO.

59.11.
SO I'LL JUST HAVE TO CLEAR THE ROAD!
YAAAHH!
59.09.
VROOOM!!

ON THE OTHER SIDE OF THE BRIDGE, ACTION MAN DISCOVERS A MESSAGE FROM DR. X!
MAP REFERENCES TO THE WHEREABOUTS OF DR. X'S 'X'-TOWERS! BUT ARE THESE THE REAL CO-ORDINATES, OR JUST A DECOY TO STOP ME REACHING THE MADNESS BOMB IN TIME?
N 11 SW 02 E 15 NE 07
The clock is ticking Action Man!
55.32.
54.22.
ZOOOOOM!!
ONLY ONE WAY TO FIND OUT! TIME TO PUT MY *SKATES* ON!
BUT DR. X HAS NO INTENTIONS OF ALLOWING ACTION MAN TO REACH THE 'X'-TOWERS!
HONNNNNK!
53.03.
JUST AS I SUSPECTED - IT'S A TRAP! AND IT'S TOO LATE FOR ME TO TURN BACK! THAT JUGGERNAUT'S NOT GOING TO STOP...!

52.46.
SO I'LL JUST HAVE TO GO AROUND IT!
GASP!
HONNNNNK!
ZOOOOOM

THIS GUY NEEDS TO BE TAUGHT A LESSON IN THE HIGHWAY CODE!
52.39.
WHOOOSSH!
52.32.
ALWAYS STOP WHEN THE LIGHT SHOWS RED!
KAA-BOOOOM!

AT THE OTHER END OF THE ALLEYWAY, ACTION MAN FINDS ANOTHER MESSAGE FROM DR. X!
FROM THE CO-ORDINATES DR. X HAS GIVEN ME, THE NEXT CLUE TO THE WHEREABOUTS OF HIS 'X'-TOWERS WILL BE FOUND AT THE GRAND PRIX MOTOR RACING CIRCUIT OF SUZUKA!
D12, A21, F3, B14, J 1.
49.12.
THE SUZUKA MOTOR RACING CIRCUIT...AND ACTION MAN HAS A SURPRISE WAITING FOR HIM!
35.48.
YOU'LL BE GIVEN THE CO-ORDINATES TO THE 'X'-TOWER, ACTION MAN...BUT ONLY IF YOU RACE AGAINST PROFESSOR GANGRENE - AND WIN!
YOU'RE CRAZY, DR. X - BUT I DON'T HAVE A CHOICE! WHAT ARE YOU WAITING FOR, GANGRENE? LET'S GO!
TEN MINUTES LATER, AND THE RACE IS ON!
25.57.
ON YOUR MARKS... GET SET...
VROOOM!
VROOOOM!

25.55.
GO!
SCREEECCCH!
TIME IS RUNNING OUT! THIS IS ONE RACE I HAVE TO WIN!
22.01.
ACTION MAN TAKES THE LEAD, DRIVING AT 250 M.P.H. AROUND THE TRACK!
I WAS EXPECTING THIS! IF GANGRENE CAN'T WIN FAIRLY, DR. X WILL ALWAYS RESORT TO CHEATING!
SCREEECCCH!
21.59.
HAHAHAHAA! IT LOOKS LIKE I'VE GIVEN ACTION MAN THE SLIP!

BUT ACTION MAN QUICKLY GETS HIS CAR UNDER CONTROL!
18.36.
IF THAT'S THE BEST THOSE TWO RATS CAN DO, THEY'RE IN FOR A DISAPPOINTMENT!
16.08.
GURRR! HE'S GAINING ON ME AGAIN!
16.02.
LET'S SEE HOW FAR HE GETS WITH FOUR FLAT TYRES! CACKLE!

15.51.
BLOW-OUT!
15.50.
CLICK!
A PUNCTURE AT THIS SPEED CAN BE DEADLY!
15.47.
BUT THE GRAND PRIX 2 HAS BEEN BUILT FOR ANY EVENTUALITY! AUTOMATIC SEALANT FOAM QUICKLY SEALS THE HOLES!

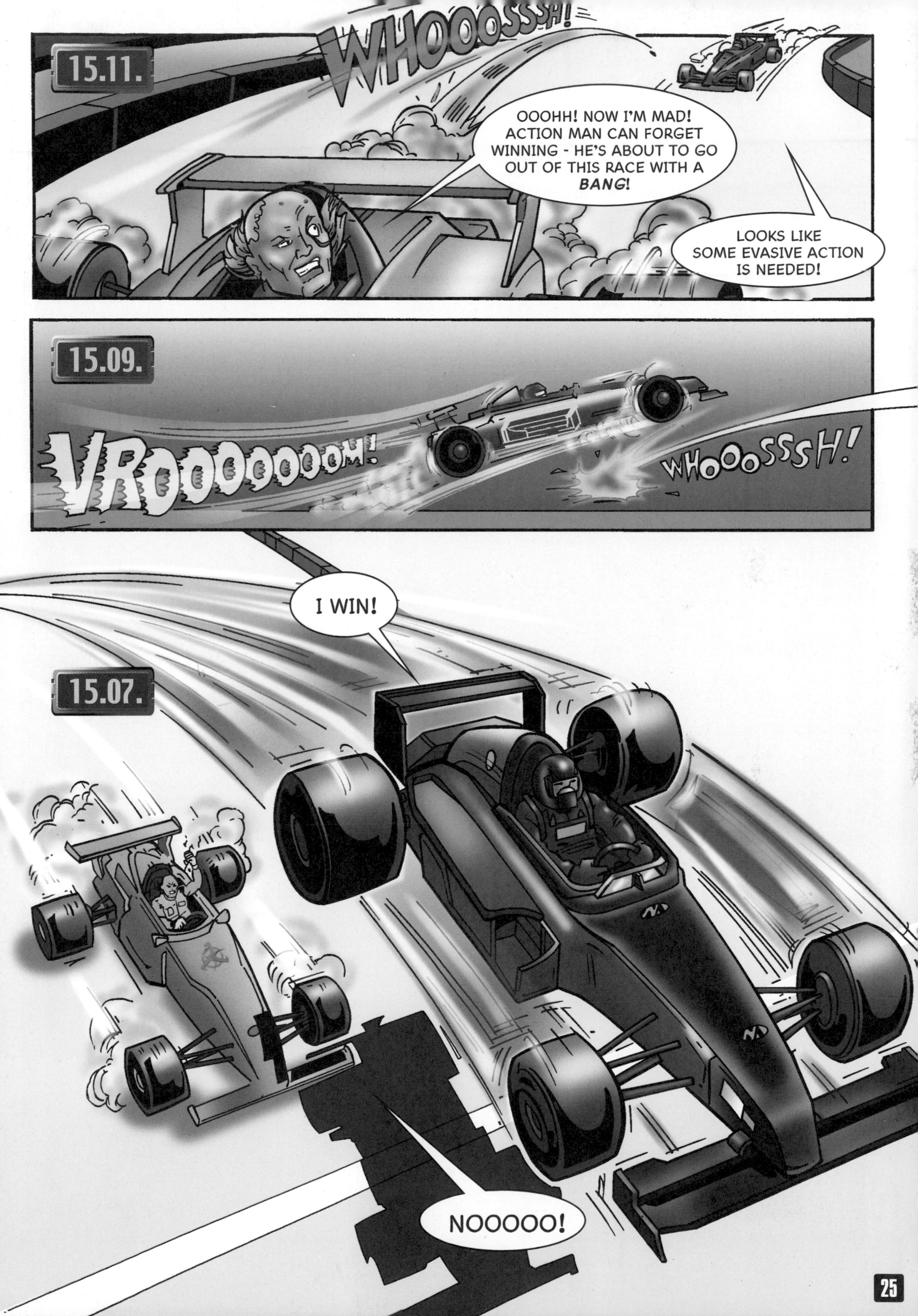
15.11.
WHOOOSSSH!
OOOHH! NOW I'M MAD! ACTION MAN CAN FORGET WINNING - HE'S ABOUT TO GO OUT OF THIS RACE WITH A *BANG*!
LOOKS LIKE SOME EVASIVE ACTION IS NEEDED!
15.09.
VROOOOOOOOM!
WHOOOSSSH!
I WIN!
15.07.
NOOOOO!

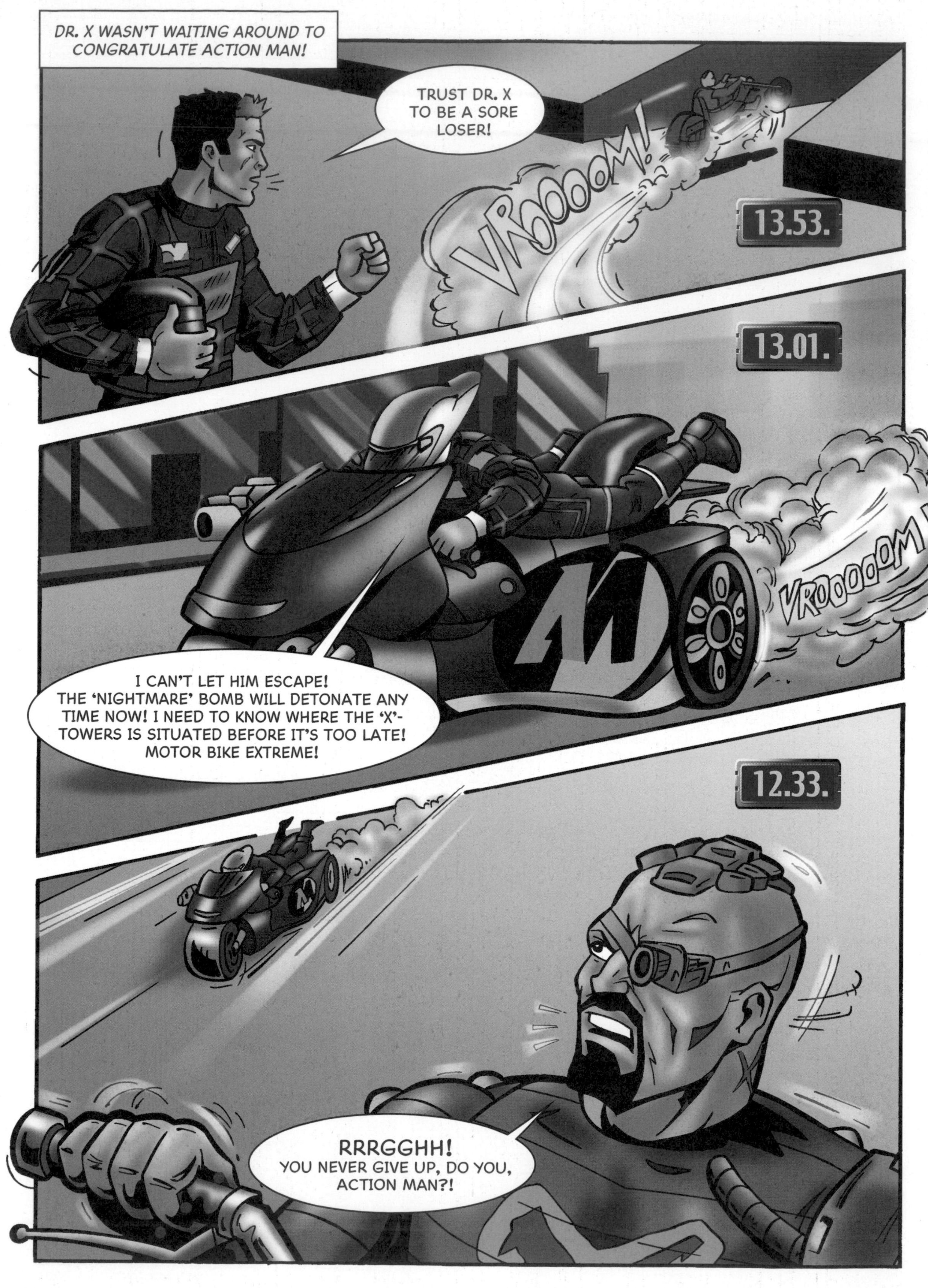

DR. X WASN'T WAITING AROUND TO CONGRATULATE ACTION MAN!
TRUST DR. X TO BE A SORE LOSER!
VROOOOM!
13.53.
13.01.
VROOOOOM!
I CAN'T LET HIM ESCAPE! THE 'NIGHTMARE' BOMB WILL DETONATE ANY TIME NOW! I NEED TO KNOW WHERE THE 'X'-TOWERS IS SITUATED BEFORE IT'S TOO LATE! MOTOR BIKE EXTREME!
12.33.
RRRGGHH! YOU NEVER GIVE UP, DO YOU, ACTION MAN?!

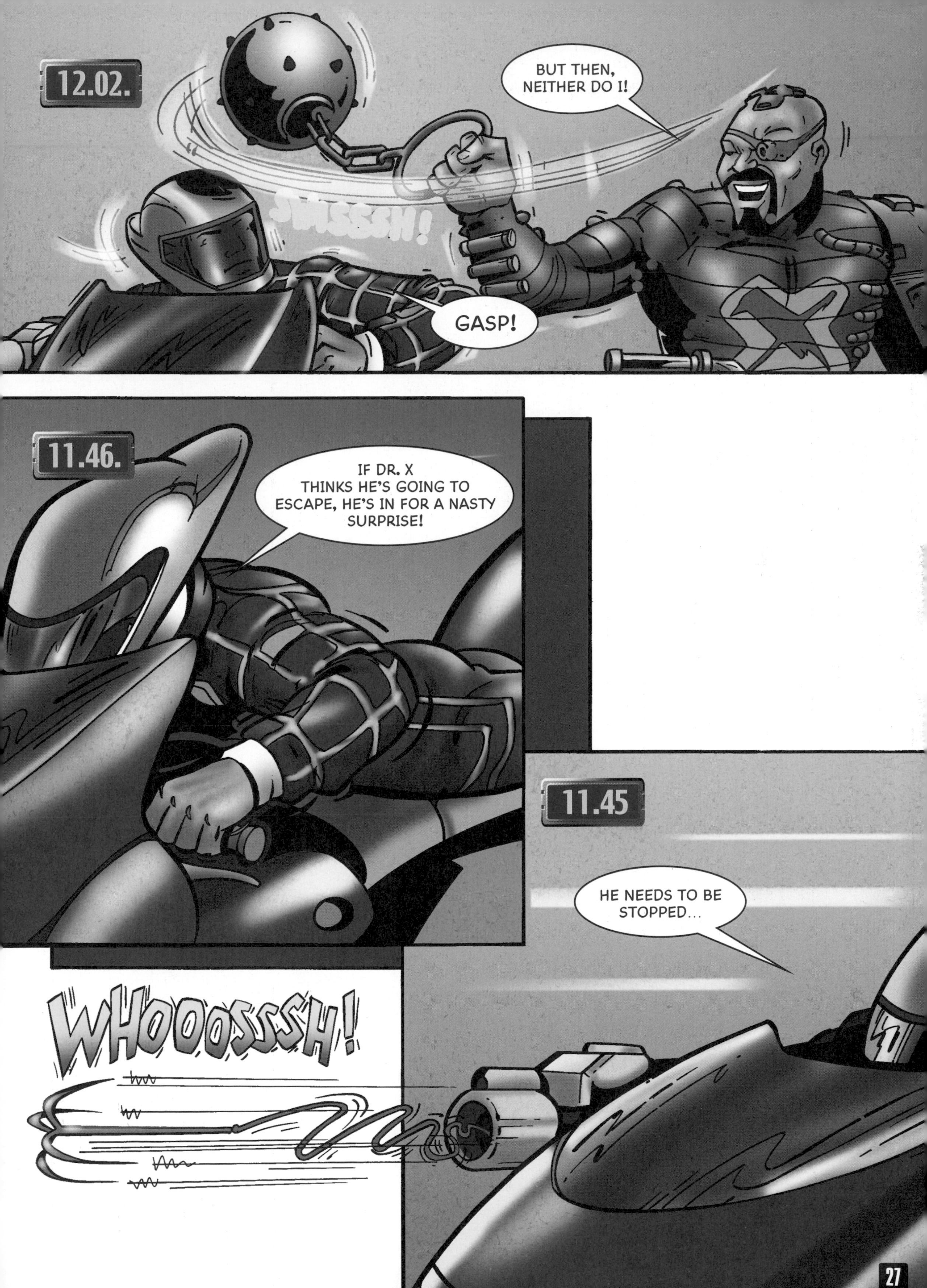

11.46.

IF DR. X THINKS HE'S GOING TO ESCAPE, HE'S IN FOR A NASTY SURPRISE!

11.45

HE NEEDS TO BE STOPPED...

WHOOOSSSH!

11.40.
TWAAANNNG!
AND FAST!
NOOOOOOO!
11.38.
YAAAAAHHH!
I ALWAYS SAID YOU WERE ***RUBBISH***, DR. X! NOW GIVE ME THE LOCATION OF YOUR 'X'-TOWER - AND NO MORE TRICKS!
10.51.
ALL RIGHT, I'LL TELL YOU! BUT YOU'D BETTER HURRY! THERE'S ONLY TEN MINUTES LEFT BEFORE MY 'NIGHTMARE' GAS IS RELEASED INTO THE AIR!
YOU MAY HAVE WON THE RACE, ACTION MAN - BUT I'LL STILL BE THE ***ULTIMATE*** WINNER! HAHAHAHAAA!
ACTION MAN

THREE MINUTES LATER...!
08.52.
IMPRESSIVE! BUT I'VE NO TIME TO ADMIRE THE ARCHITECTURE! I'VE ONLY FIVE MINUTES LEFT TO DEFUSE THAT BOMB!
SOON, IN THE CORRIDORS OF THE 'X'-TOWERS...! 
05.39.
DR. X SAYS THE BOMB IS PLANTED IN THE ROYAL SUITE! TIME IS PRECIOUS, BUT I CAN'T JUST RUSH IN! HE MIGHT HAVE ARMED THIS PLACE WITH DEADLY BOOBY-TRAPS!
BLEEP!
BLEEP!
BLEEP!
MY METAL DETECTOR ISNT PICKING ANYTHING UP. STRANGE, IT'S NOT LIKE DR. X TO GIVE IN SO EASILY!

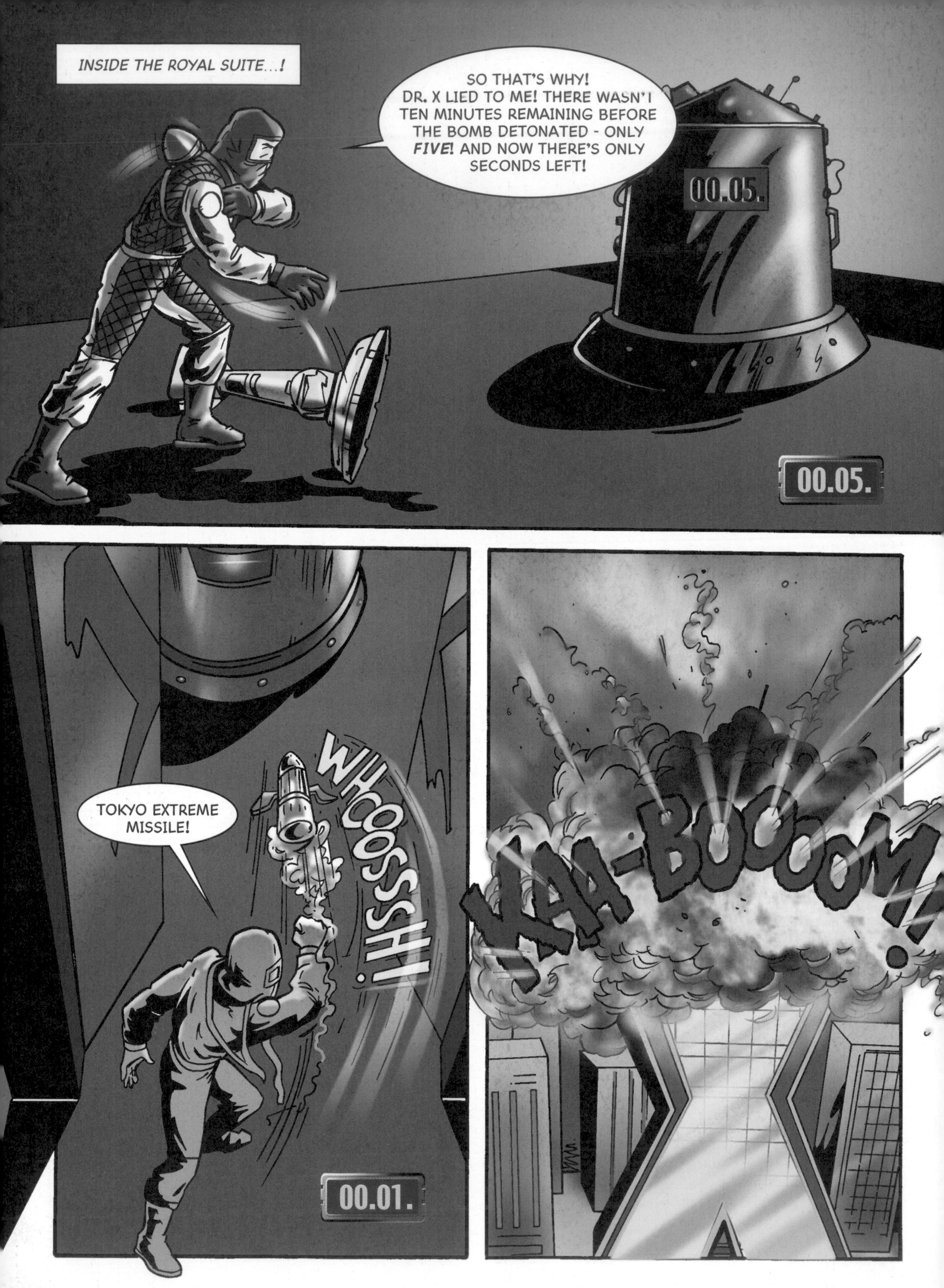

INSIDE THE ROYAL SUITE...!

SO THAT'S WHY! DR. X LIED TO ME! THERE WASN'T TEN MINUTES REMAINING BEFORE THE BOMB DETONATED - ONLY *FIVE*! AND NOW THERE'S ONLY SECONDS LEFT!

00.05.

00.05.

THE 'NIGHTMARE' GAS WAS DESTROYED BY THE BLISTERING HEAT OF THAT DOUBLE-STRENGTH EXPLOSION! DR.X THOUGHT HE COULD WIN BY CHEATING...BUT CHEATS NEVER PROSER!
SUDDENLY, ACTION MAN RECEIVES AN URGENT MESSAGE ON HIS PDA...!
HMM, CHEATS MIGHT NEVER PROSPER, BUT, IT SEEMS, THEY NEVER GIVE UP, EITHER...! WHAT MAD SCHEME FOR WORLD DOMINATION IS DR. X UP TO NOW...?!
DOCTOR
X
TEMPEST

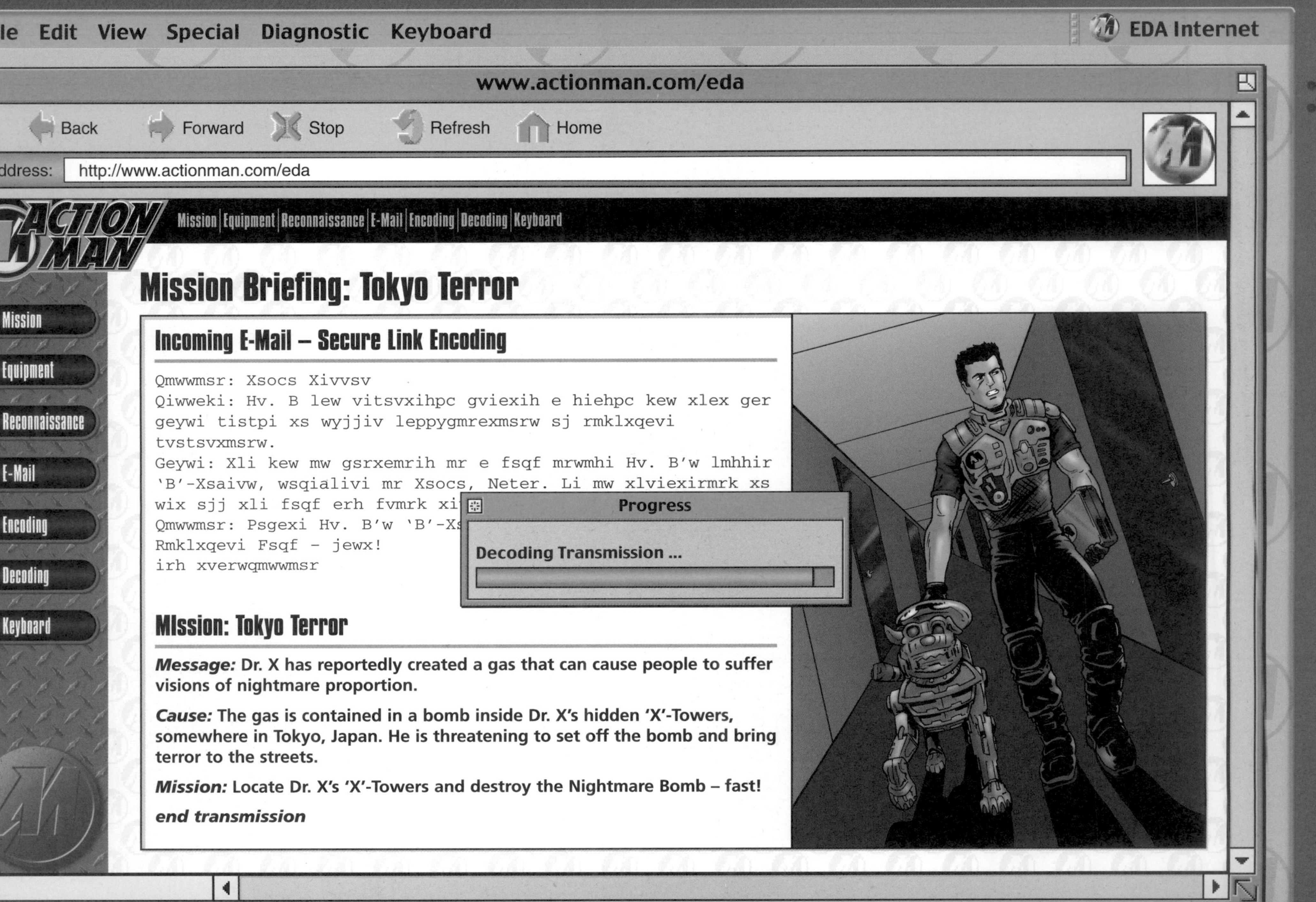
File Edit View Special Diagnostic Keyboard
EDA Internet
www.actionman.com/eda
Back Forward Stop Refresh Home
Address: http://www.actionman.com/eda
ACTION MAN
Mission | Equipment | Reconnaissance | E-Mail | Encoding | Decoding | Keyboard
Mission
Equipment
Reconnaissance
E-Mail
Encoding
Decoding
Keyboard
Mission Briefing: Tokyo Terror
Incoming E-Mail – Secure Link Encoding
Qmwwmsr: Xsocs Xivvsv
Qiwweki: Hv. B lew vitsvxihpc gviexih e hiehpc kew xlex ger geywi tistpi xs wyjjiv leppygmrexmsrw sj rmklxqevi tvstsvxmsrw.
Geywi: Xli kew mw gsrxemrih mr e fsqf mrwmhi Hv. B'w lmhhir 'B'-Xsaivw, wsqialivi mr Xsocs, Neter. Li mw xlviexirmrk xs wix sjj xli fsqf erh fvmrk xi
Qmwwmsr: Psgexi Hv. B'w 'B'-Xs
Rmklxqevi Fsqf – jewx!
irh xverwqmwwmsr
Progress
Decoding Transmission ...
Mission: Tokyo Terror
Message: Dr. X has reportedly created a gas that can cause people to suffer visions of nightmare proportion.
Cause: The gas is contained in a bomb inside Dr. X's hidden 'X'-Towers, somewhere in Tokyo, Japan. He is threatening to set off the bomb and bring terror to the streets.
Mission: Locate Dr. X's 'X'-Towers and destroy the Nightmare Bomb – fast!
end transmission

File Edit View Special Diagnostic Keyboard EDA Internet

www.actionman.com/eda

Back Forward Stop Refresh Home

Address: http://www.actionman.com/eda

ACTION MAN

Mission | Equipment | Reconnaissance | E-Mail | Encoding | Decoding | Keyboard

Mission

Equipment

Reconnaissance

E-Mail

Encoding

Decoding

Keyboard

Geographical Reconnaissance Data

Tokyo

Capital city of Japan

Location: Situated on Honshu Island

Population: Approximately 8 million

History: Founded in the 16th century as Yedo (or Edo) it was renamed when the Emperor of the time moved his court here from Kyoto in 1868

Landmarks: The Sumida River delta separates the city from its suburb of Honjo

Buildings of note: The Imperial Palace, National Diet
7th century Asakusa Kannon Temple, Tokyo Disneyland

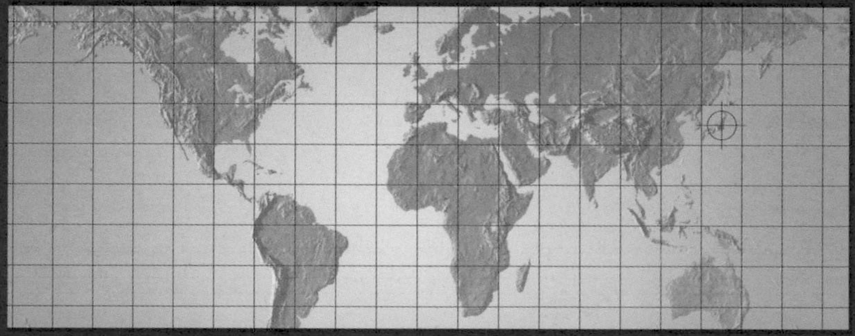

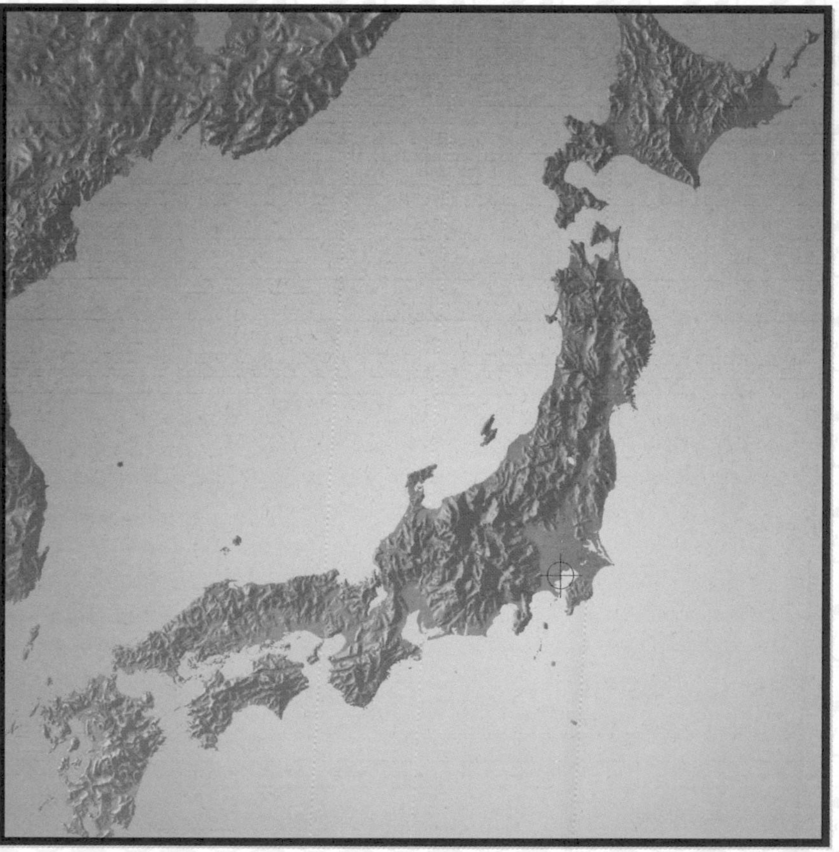

INITIATE COMMS. MISSION STATUS

MIC

AM2002PDA

File Edit View Special Diagnostic Keyboard

EDA Internet

www.actionman.com/eda

Back Forward Stop Refresh Home

Address: http://www.actionman.com/eda

ACTION MAN

Mission | Equipment | Reconnaissance | E-Mail | Encoding | Decoding | Keyboard

Mission

Equipment

Reconnaissance

E-Mail

Encoding

Decoding

Keyboard

Mission Data: Equipment

Grand Prix

Frame:	Carbon fibre with aluminium frame
Engine:	twin turbo engine with solid fuel rocket boosters
EFT:	Epoxy resin fluid-filled automatic re-sealant tyres in case of blow-outs
Thrust:	400lb thrust for manoeuvrability
Top Speed:	0-250 kph in nine seconds
Weapons:	Two Sidewinder missiles.

The race is on!

File Edit View Special Diagnostic Keyboard EDA Internet

www.actionman.com/eda

Back Forward Stop Refresh Home

Address: http://www.actionman.com/eda

ACTION MAN

Mission | Equipment | Reconnaissance | E-Mail | Encoding | Decoding | Keyboard

Mission

Equipment

Reconnaissance

E-Mail

Encoding

Decoding

Keyboard

Mission Data: Equipment

Motorbike Extreme

Frame:	Carbon fibre with magnesium composite with adjustable ceramic shock absorbers
Engine:	3200cc engine with added turbo boosters
EFT:	Epoxy resin fluid-filled tyres
AGS:	32 gear automatic gearing system with manual override handlebar grip
Top Speed:	270 mph
Weapons:	3 heat-seeking Sidewinder missiles

On your bike!

INITIATE COMMS. MISSION STATUS

MIC

AM2002PDA

ACTION MAN

MONSTER FROM THE DEEP!

MISSION LOG. 11. 17 HOURS. THE ANTARCTIC. HOT ON THE TRAIL OF DR. X, ACTION MAN SUDDENLY FINDS THAT IT IS **HE** WHO IS BEING PURSUED...!
GET HIM!
VROOM!
IT LOOKS LIKE DR. X HAS SENT OUT A WELCOMING COMMITTEE! WHAT A SURPRISE!

VROOOMM!
LET'S SEE IF THEIR SNOW-MOBILES ARE ANY MATCH FOR MY ARCTIC RALLY CAR!
VROOOMM!

HMM!
GUESS NOT!
YAAAAHHH!
WHUUMMMP!
BUT, UP AHEAD...!
HERE HE COMES!
HA! WE'LL BLAST HIM INTO TINY PIECES!
FIRE!
WHOOOSSSH!

I TAKE IT THESE GUYS AREN'T MEMBERS OF MY FAN CLUB!
KAA-BOOOOM!
SCREEEECCH!
THAT'S CARELESS OF THEM! THEY SEEM TO HAVE LOST THEIR MISSILES! PERHAPS THEY'D LIKE ONE OF MINE?
WHOOOSSSH!

OH, NOOO!
THEN AGAIN, PERHAPS NOT!
CHUCKLE!
FWOOOSSSH!
YAAAGGGHHH!
BUT ACTION MAN ISN'T OUT OF DANGER YET!
BLOCK HIM IN! HE WON'T ESCAPE US THIS TIME!

TIME TO PUT MY FOOT DOWN!
A HIGHLY TRAINED OPERATIVE, ACTION MAN EASILY OUT-MANOEURVES HIS DEADLY PURSUERS...!
AAAAHHH!
VROOOOOM!

THAT'LL TEACH THEM NOT TO WEAR THEIR SEATBELTS!
YAAARRGGGHH!
SMAAASSSH!
WITH DR. X'S MEN LAYING SENSELESS, ACTION MAN PAUSES TO ACCESS INFORMATION FROM HIS PDA...!
THE PDA IS DIRECTLY LINKED TO AN ORBITAL TRACKING SATELLITE, ALLOWING ME TO ACCURATELY PINPOINT DR. X`S SECRET BASE!
SW 23, N 16, NW 08, SE 15
CLEVER! ONLY A MADMAN LIKE DR. X COULD HIDE HIMSELF AWAY *INSIDE* AN ICEBERG! AND IF HE`S THERE, HIS GIANT SEA MONSTER MUST BE CLOSE BY!

ACTION MAN KNOWS SPEED IS OF THE ESSENCE! HE REACHES AN ICE CAVE, WHERE HIS ARCTIC SURF BIKE IS WAITING FOR HIM...!
DR. X'S BASE IS ALMOST FORTY KLICKS AWAY! BUT WITH MY ARCTIC SURF BIKE I SHOULD BE THERE IN NO TIME!
WHOOOSSSH!
HOWEVER, AS ACTION MAN REACHES THE LOCATION - !
WHAT THE...?!
KAA-BOOOOM!

WHUP-WHUP-WHUP!
HAHAHAAA! YOU'RE GOING NOWHERE, ACTION MAN...EXCEPT TO YOUR DOOM!
PROFESSOR GANGRENE!

I HOPE YOU HAVE THE *STOMACH* FOR A FIGHT, ACTION MAN, BECAUSE I CERTAINLY HAVE! HAHAHAA!
SQUEELLCCH!
I'M GOING TO ENJOY DESTROYING YOU, ACTION MAN! IN FACT...
WHOOOSSSH!

THERE'S NO WAY TO AVOID THAT FIREBALL...
...IT'S GOING TO BE A *BLAST*! HAHAHAA!
KAA-BOOOM!
...SO I'LL JUST HAVE TO GO *OVER* IT!
WHOOOSSSH!
CURSES! HE ESCAPED MY ATTACK, AND I HAVE NO MORE MISSILES LEFT! BUT IF I CAN'T BLOW HIM AWAY...

I'LL JUST HAVE TO RUN HIM DOWN, INSTEAD!
WHUP-WHUP-WHUP!
PROFESSOR GANGRENE WANTS TO PLAY A GAME OF 'FOLLOW-MY-LEADER', DOES HE?

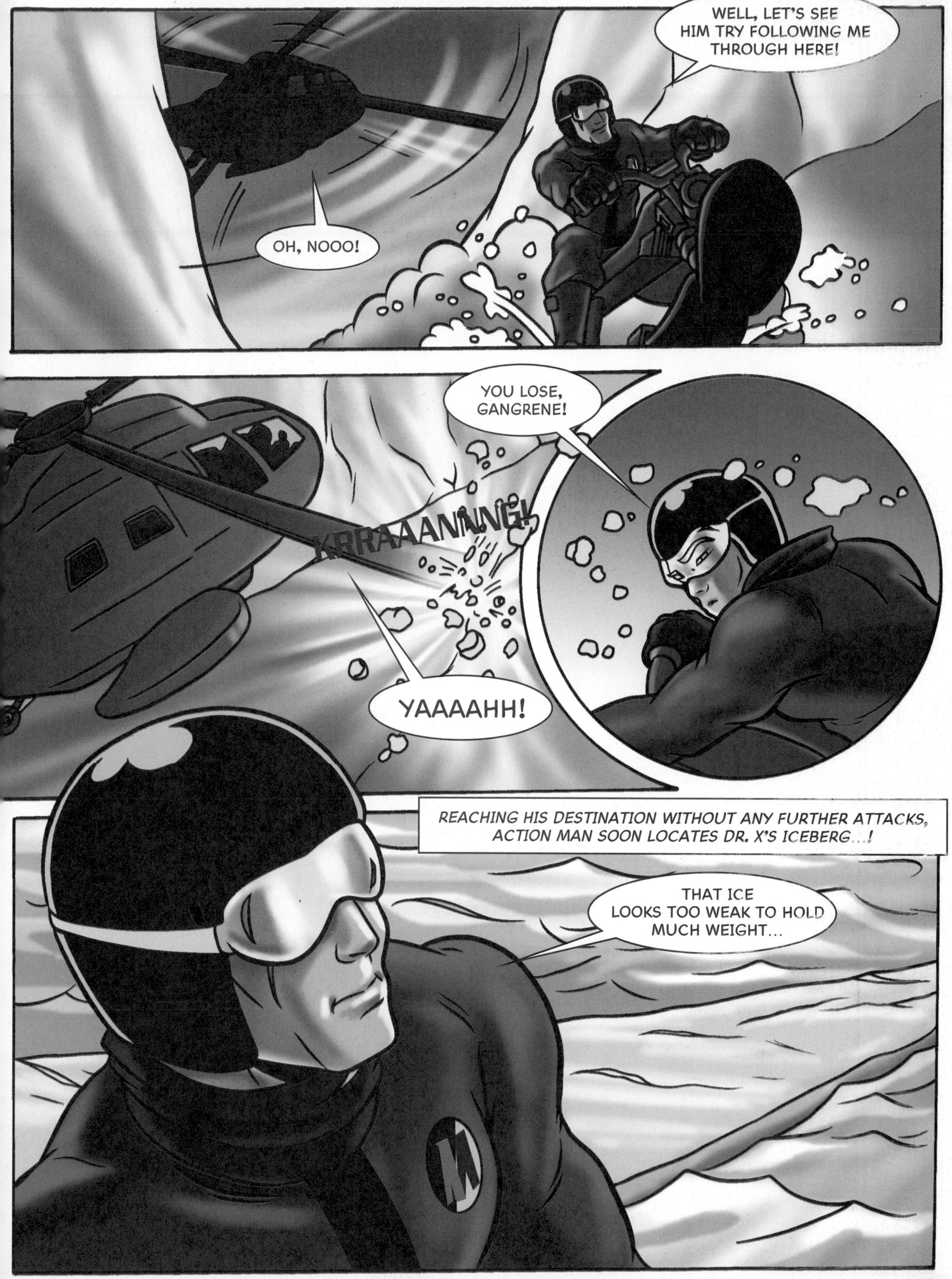

YOU LOSE, GANGRENE!

KRRAAANNNG!

YAAAAHH!

REACHING HIS DESTINATION WITHOUT ANY FURTHER ATTACKS, ACTION MAN SOON LOCATES DR. X'S ICEBERG...!

THAT ICE LOOKS TOO WEAK TO HOLD MUCH WEIGHT...

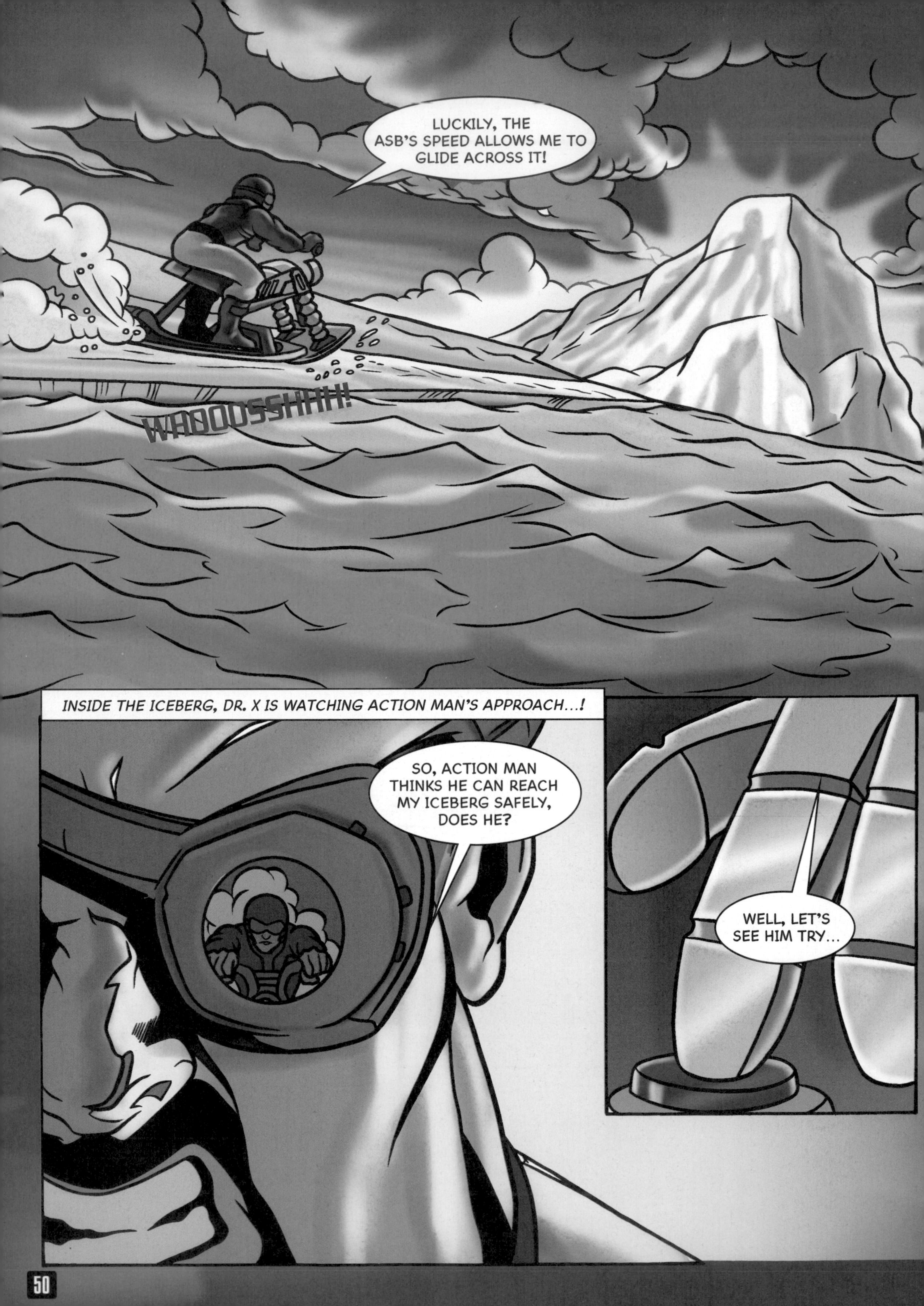
LUCKILY, THE ASB'S SPEED ALLOWS ME TO GLIDE ACROSS IT!
WHOOOSSHHH!
INSIDE THE ICEBERG, DR. X IS WATCHING ACTION MAN'S APPROACH...!
SO, ACTION MAN THINKS HE CAN REACH MY ICEBERG SAFELY, DOES HE?
WELL, LET'S SEE HIM TRY...

...WHEN I MOVE THE ICEBERG FURTHER AWAY! HAHAHAAA!
IF I DROP INTO THE WATER, I'LL FREEZE IN MOMENTS!
SO I'D BETTER MAKE SURE I DON'T!
TWAANNNG!
I'M STARTING TO GET THE FEELING THAT DR. X DOESN'T WANT MY COMPANY! TOO BAD, BECAUSE HE'S ABOUT TO GET IT!
THUUDD!

GRRRR!
YOU WANT TO MEET MY GENETICALLY ENGINEERED SEA MONSTER, ACTION MAN? THE ONE WITH WHICH I SHALL RULE THE VERY SEAS THEMSELVES?!!
LANDING SAFELY ON A LEDGE, ACTION MAN QUICKLY SCALES THE ICEBERG WITH HIS ARCTIC CLIMBER EQUIPMENT!
THEN SO YOU SHALL! DESTROY HIM, MY PET! DESTROY HIM!!! HAHAHAHAAAAAA!!
GASP!
RRRRRRHHH!

RRRRRRHHH!
IF THAT MONSTER'S TENTACLES GET A GRIP ON ME, I'M DONE FOR!
SO I'D BETTER MAKE SURE THEY DON'T!
ACTION MAN LANDS BACK ON HIS ARCTIC SURF BIKE...
IT'S ABOUT TIME I WRAPPED UP THIS CASE...

...BY WRAPPING THIS MONSTER UP IN KNOTS!
TWAANNNG!
WHUWIP!
RRRRRRHHH?
AND NOW TO SEND THE MONSTER BACK WHERE IT BELONGS...
WHOOOSSSH!
RRRRRRHHH!
TO THE VERY BOTTOM OF THE OCEAN!

BY THE TIME ACTION MAN BREAKS INTO THE ICEBERG, DR. X HAS ALREADY ESCAPED!
TRUST DR. X TO RUN AWAY! BUT AT LEAST HIS MONSTER CAN NO LONGER THREATEN SHIPPING IN THIS AREA!
AND FROM THE INCOMING MESSAGE I'M RECEIVING FROM MY PDA, DR. X AND I SHALL BE MEETING AGAIN...VERY SOON!
THE END

File Edit View Special Diagnostic Keyboard EDA Internet

www.actionman.com/eda

Back Forward Stop Refresh Home

Address: http://www.actionman.com/eda

ACTION MAN

Mission | Equipment | Reconnaissance | E-Mail | Encoding | Decoding | Keyboard

Mission Debriefing

To give Action Man more time to prepare for his next mission, can you extract and download the key information from the last two missions he has just completed? Answer the questions by ticking the correct solution.

1) In what location was Dr. X's giant sea monster attacking shipping?

A) The Indian Ocean ☐
B) The Antarctic ☐
C) The Mediterranean Sea ☐

2) When first arriving in the Antarctic, what vehicle does Action Man use to escape his pursuers?

A) Arctic Rally Car ☐
B) Arctic Surf Bike ☐
C) Desert Buggy ☐

3) Where was Dr. X`s base located in the Antarctic?

A) Inside a submarine ☐
B) Behind a cliff face ☐
C) Inside an iceberg ☐

4) From where does Professor Gangrene attack Action Man?

A) The sea ☐
B) On land ☐
C) The air ☐

5) In what city does Dr. X threaten to release the deadly 'Nightmare' gas?

A) Sydney, Australia ☐
B) Tokyo, Japan ☐
C) London, England ☐

6) In what location was Dr. X's Nightmare Bomb hidden?

A) The Imperial Palace ☐
B) Disneyland ☐
C) The `X`-Towers ☐

7) Action Man races Professor Gangrene at the Suzuka Racing Circuit in Japan in his...?

A) Grand Prix 2 car ☐
B) Argo ☐
C) Kart Extreme ☐

8) How was the Nightmare Bomb deactivated?

A) The bomb was a dud ☐
B) In searing blast from Action Man's Tokyo Extreme missile ☐
c) Action Man defused the bomb, just in time ☐

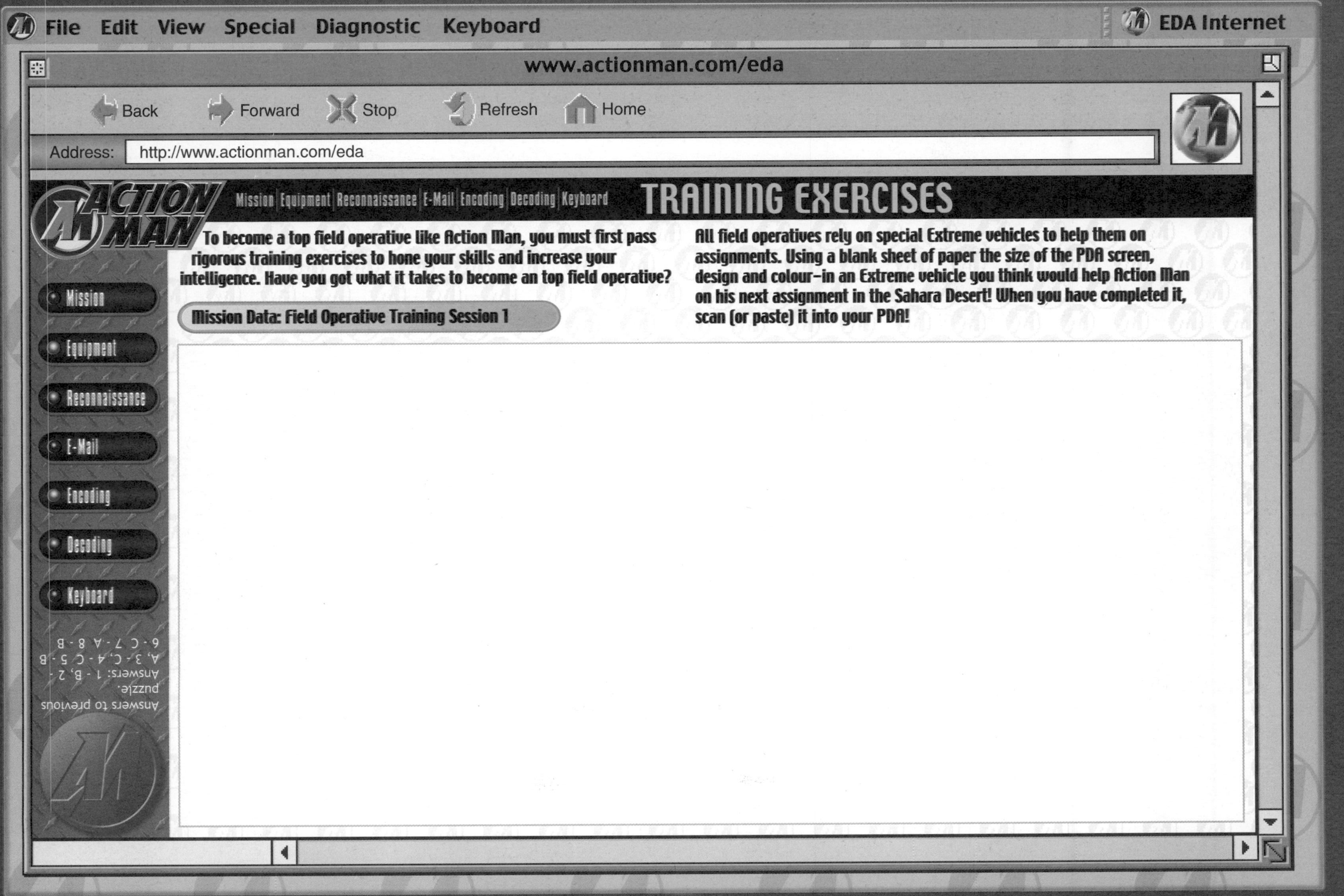
File Edit View Special Diagnostic Keyboard
EDA Internet
www.actionman.com/eda
Back
Forward
Stop
Refresh
Home
Address: http://www.actionman.com/eda
ACTION MAN
Mission | Equipment | Reconnaissance | E-Mail | Encoding | Decoding | Keyboard
TRAINING EXERCISES
To become a top field operative like Action Man, you must first pass rigorous training exercises to hone your skills and increase your intelligence. Have you got what it takes to become an top field operative?
Mission Data: Field Operative Training Session 1
All field operatives rely on special Extreme vehicles to help them on assignments. Using a blank sheet of paper the size of the PDA screen, design and colour-in an Extreme vehicle you think would help Action Man on his next assignment in the Sahara Desert! When you have completed it, scan (or paste) it into your PDA!
Mission
Equipment
Reconnaissance
E-Mail
Encoding
Decoding
Keyboard
Answers to previous puzzle.
Answers: 1 - B, 2 - A, 3 - C, 4 - C 5 - B 6 - C 7 - A 8 - B
INITIATE
COMMS.
MISSION
STATUS
MIC
AM2002PDA

File Edit View Special Diagnostic Keyboard — EDA Internet

www.actionman.com/eda

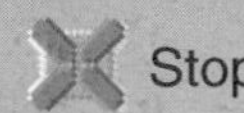 Back · Forward · 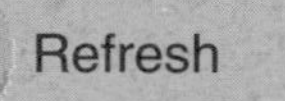 Stop ·   Refresh · Home

Address: http://www.actionman.com/eda

ACTION MAN — Mission | Equipment | Reconnaissance | E-Mail | Encoding | Decoding | Keyboard

Mission Briefing: Weather Warriors

Incoming E-Mail – Secure Link Encoding

Qmwwmsr: Aiexliv Aevvmsvw
Qiwweki: Hv. B erh Xiqtiwx lezi xeoir sziv e xst wigvix kszivrqirx viwievgl Fmshsqi jegmpmxc mr xli Weleve Hiwivx. Xli Fmshsqi mw fimrk ywih xs vigsvh hexe sr glerkmrk aiexliv texxivrw egvsww xli asvph.
Geywi: Xlivi mw e wyhhir zmspirx glerki sj aiexliv egxmzmxc sziv xli Weleve Hiwivx. Mx mw fipmizih xlex Xiqtiwx mw glerrippmrk lmw pmklxrmrk tsaivw xlvsykl xli Fmshsqi'w AGH (Aiexliv Gsrhymx Hizmgi)
asvph'w aiexliv.
Qmwwmsr: Mj Hv. B ger gsrxvsp xli aiexliv
wxsttih. Ibxviqi jsvgi qec fi rigiwwevc!
irh xverwqmwwmsr

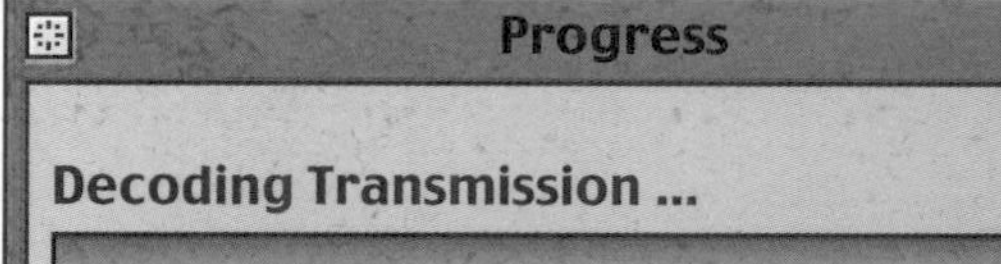

Mission: Weather Warriors

Message: **Dr. X and Tempest have taken over a top secret government research Biodome facility in the Sahara Desert. The Biodome is being used to record data on changing weather patterns across the world.**

Cause: **There is a sudden violent change of weather activity over the Sahara Desert. It is believed that Tempest is channelling his lightning powers through the Biodome's WCD (Weather Conduit Device) to enable Dr. X to control the world's weather.**

Mission: **If Dr. X can control the weather he can rule the world. He must be stopped. Extreme force may be necessary!**

end transmission

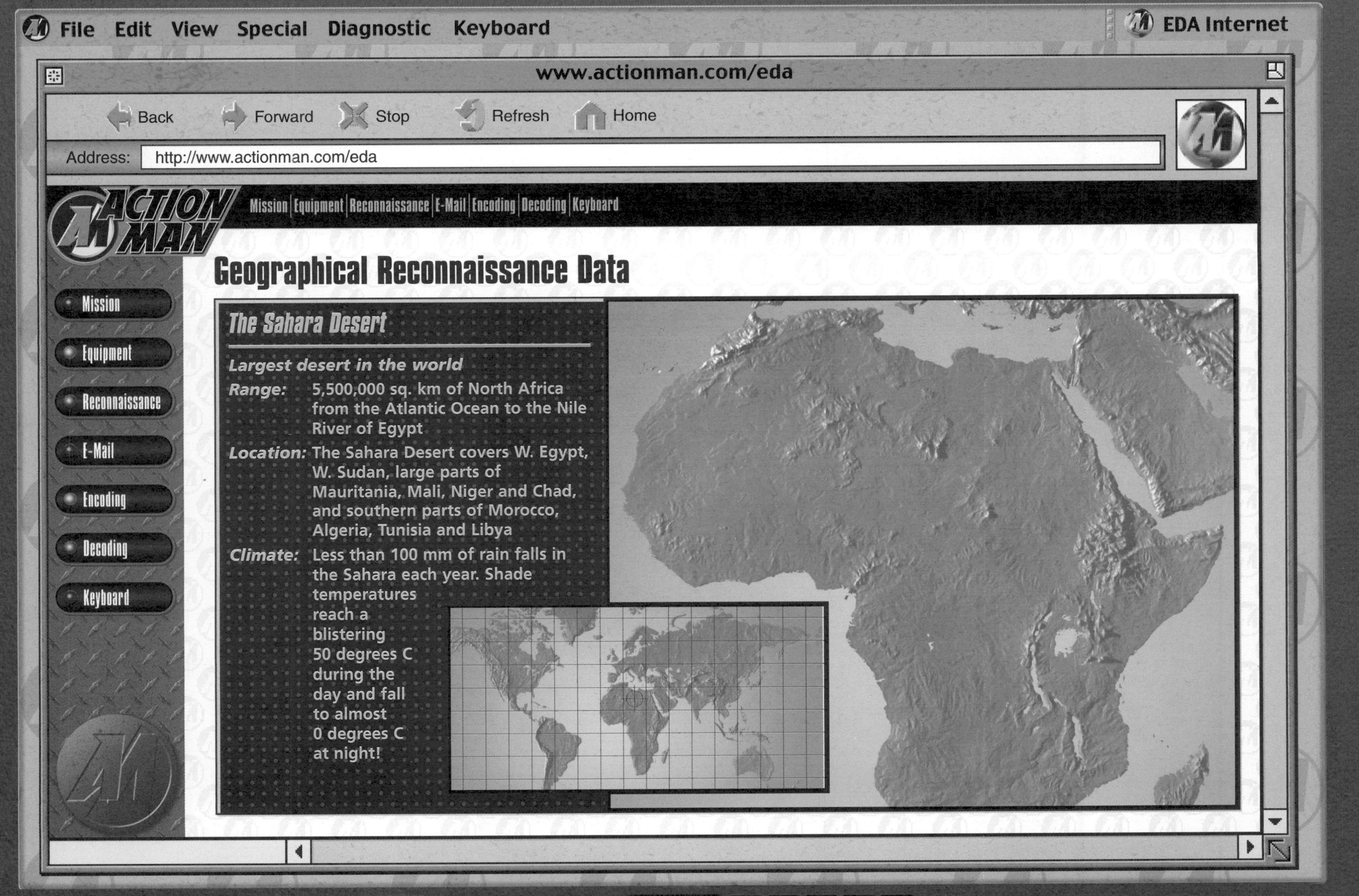

File Edit View Special Diagnostic Keyboard
EDA Internet
www.actionman.com/eda
Back Forward Stop Refresh Home
Address: http://www.actionman.com/eda
ACTION MAN
Mission | Equipment | Reconnaissance | E-Mail | Encoding | Decoding | Keyboard
Mission
Equipment
Reconnaissance
E-Mail
Encoding
Decoding
Keyboard
Geographical Reconnaissance Data
The Sahara Desert
Largest desert in the world
Range: 5,500,000 sq. km of North Africa from the Atlantic Ocean to the Nile River of Egypt
Location: The Sahara Desert covers W. Egypt, W. Sudan, large parts of Mauritania, Mali, Niger and Chad, and southern parts of Morocco, Algeria, Tunisia and Libya
Climate: Less than 100 mm of rain falls in the Sahara each year. Shade temperatures reach a blistering 50 degrees C during the day and fall to almost 0 degrees C at night!
INITIATE
COMMS.
MISSION
STATUS
MIC
AM2002PDA

File Edit View Special Diagnostic Keyboard

EDA Internet

www.actionman.com/eda

Back Forward Stop Refresh Home

Address: http://www.actionman.com/eda

ACTION MAN

Mission | Equipment | Reconnaissance | E-Mail | Encoding | Decoding | Keyboard

Mission

Equipment

Reconnaissance

E-Mail

Encoding

Decoding

Keyboard

Mission Data: Equipment

Air Surfer

Parafoil: Canopy is made from lightweight yet extremely strong and durable silk material attached to an aluminium frame, and whose direction is controlled by a steering line

Surfboard: The surfboard base of the Air Surfer is made from tough, lightweight, impact resilient polycarbonate material

Speed of Descent: Between 50-120 mph depending on air currents and wind direction

Weapons: None – the Air Surfer is an ariel transport vehicle only

Time to drop in!

Silk canopy

Snowboard

File Edit View Special Diagnostic Keyboard
EDA Internet
www.actionman.com/eda
Back Forward Stop Refresh Home
Address: http://www.actionman.com/eda
ACTION MAN
Mission | Equipment | Reconnaissance | E-Mail | Encoding | Decoding | Keyboard
Mission
Equipment
Reconnaissance
E-Mail
Encoding
Decoding
Keyboard
Mission Data: Equipment
Desert Buggy
Frame: Carbon fibre bonded to aluminium frame with kevlar armour
EFT: Epoxy resin fluid-filled all-terrain tyres
Engine: Mid mounted x15 with twin turbos
Navigation: GPS (Global Positioning System)
Top Speed: 135 mph
Weapons: Two multipurpose Sidewinder missiles
The heat is on!
Aluminium frame
All-terrain tyres
Twin turbos
Sidewinders
INITIATE
COMMS.
MISSION
STATUS
MIC
AM2002PDA

ACTION MAN
WEATHER WARRIORS!

WITH DR. X'S MADNESS BOMB DESTROYED, ACTION MAN SEARCHES THE 'X'-TOWERS FOR CLUES AS DR. X'S WHEREABOUTS!
IF THERE ARE ANY MORE TRAPS OR SURPRISES WAITING FOR ME INSIDE THIS BUILDING, MY CYBER DOG WILL SOON SNIFF THEM OUT!
SNIFF! SNIFF!

COMPUTER ROOM
HMM, THAT COMPUTER ROOM COULD HOLD THE INFORMATION I'M LOOKING FOR! BUT MY CYBER DOG IS WARNING ME OF DANGER!
RRRRRRHHH!
THE CYBER DOG CAN SNIFF OUT PEOPLE SOME DISTANCE AWAY!
BEHIND THE DOORS...!
HA! WHEN ACTION MAN ENTERS THIS ROOM, HE'LL NEVER KNOW WHAT HIT HIM!
BUT ACTION MAN IS TAKING NO CHANCES!
THIS IS ONE DOG WHOSE BITE REALLY IS WORSE THAN ITS BARK!
WHOOOSSH!

KAR-BOOOOM!
JUST AS I THOUGHT! AN AMBUSH! I'LL BET THEY WISH THEY HADN'T BOTHERED!
GROAN!
NOW TO ACCESS THE INFORMATION STORED IN THESE COMPUTERS. I NEED TO FIND OUT HOW DR. X AND TEMPEST COULD UPSET THE WEATHER PATTERNS SO EASILY! IF THEY'RE NOT STOPPED, THEY COULD DESTROY THE STABILITY OF THE WORLD'S ECOSYSTEMS!

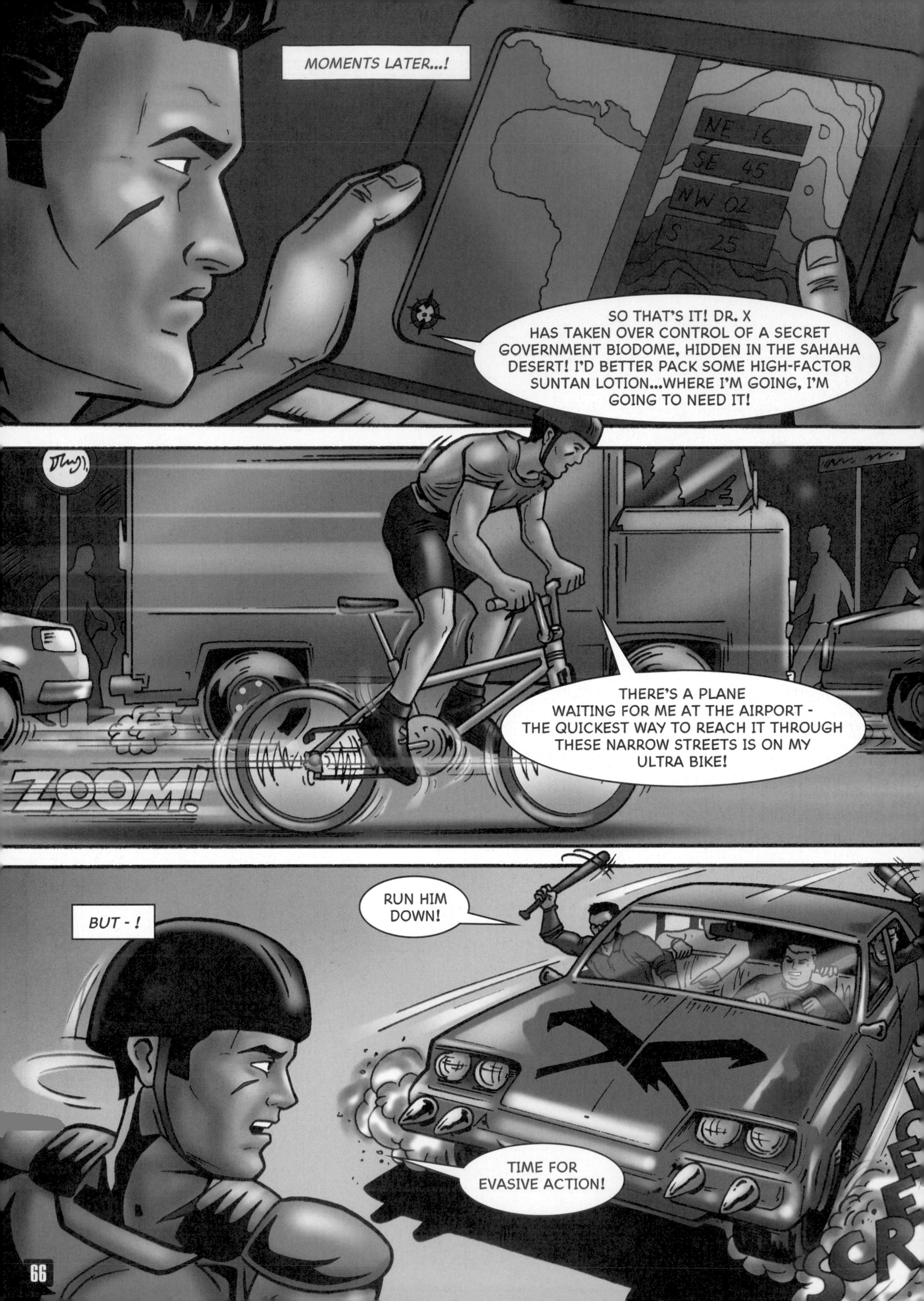
MOMENTS LATER...!
NE 16
SE 45
NW 02
S 25
SO THAT'S IT! DR. X HAS TAKEN OVER CONTROL OF A SECRET GOVERNMENT BIODOME, HIDDEN IN THE SAHAHA DESERT! I'D BETTER PACK SOME HIGH-FACTOR SUNTAN LOTION...WHERE I'M GOING, I'M GOING TO NEED IT!
THERE'S A PLANE WAITING FOR ME AT THE AIRPORT - THE QUICKEST WAY TO REACH IT THROUGH THESE NARROW STREETS IS ON MY ULTRA BIKE!
ZOOM!
BUT - !
RUN HIM DOWN!
TIME FOR EVASIVE ACTION!

YOU DWEEBS SHOULD TAKE UP CYCLING! IT'S A LOT HEALTHIER...
SMASH! 
...AND THE WAY YOU DRIVE, IT WOULD BE A LOT LESS DANGEROUS!
YAAAAGGHH!

REACHING TOKYO AIRPORT, ACTION MAN TAKES OFF FOR HIS DESTINATION! HOURS LATER, HE FINDS HIMSELF FLYING DOWN TOWARDS THE BURNING SANDS OF THE SAHAHA DESERT ON HIS MAGNIFICENT AIR SURFER...!
WHOOOSH!
THIS IS THE ONLY WAY TO TRAVEL!
CHUCKLE!

BUT, WAITING BELOW...!
WHOO-HOO! ACTION MAN'S GONNA GET THE SHOCK OF HIS LIFE AFTER MY LIGHTNING STAFFS TURN UP THE HEAT! HIS GOOSE IS AS GOOD AS COOKED!
ZZZZZZKKKKK!
TEMPEST CAN CONTROL THE WEATHER SYSTEMS OF THE WORLD USING HIS LIGHTNING STAFFS!
KAA-BOOM!
WELL, THIS IS THE SAHARA, SO I WAS EXPECTING A *WARM* RECEPTION!
KAA-BOOM!

TEMPEST'S NOT THE ONLY ONE WHOSE BROUGHT HIS TOYS ALONG TO PLAY WITH!
SSSSSSSSSSSSHHHH!
LET'S SEE HOW MUCH FUN HE GETS FROM MY DISC EXTREME!
HA! PITIFUL, ACTION MAN! YOU MUST BE DESPERATE! THAT PUNY THING CAN'T HURT MY LIGHTNING STAFFS!

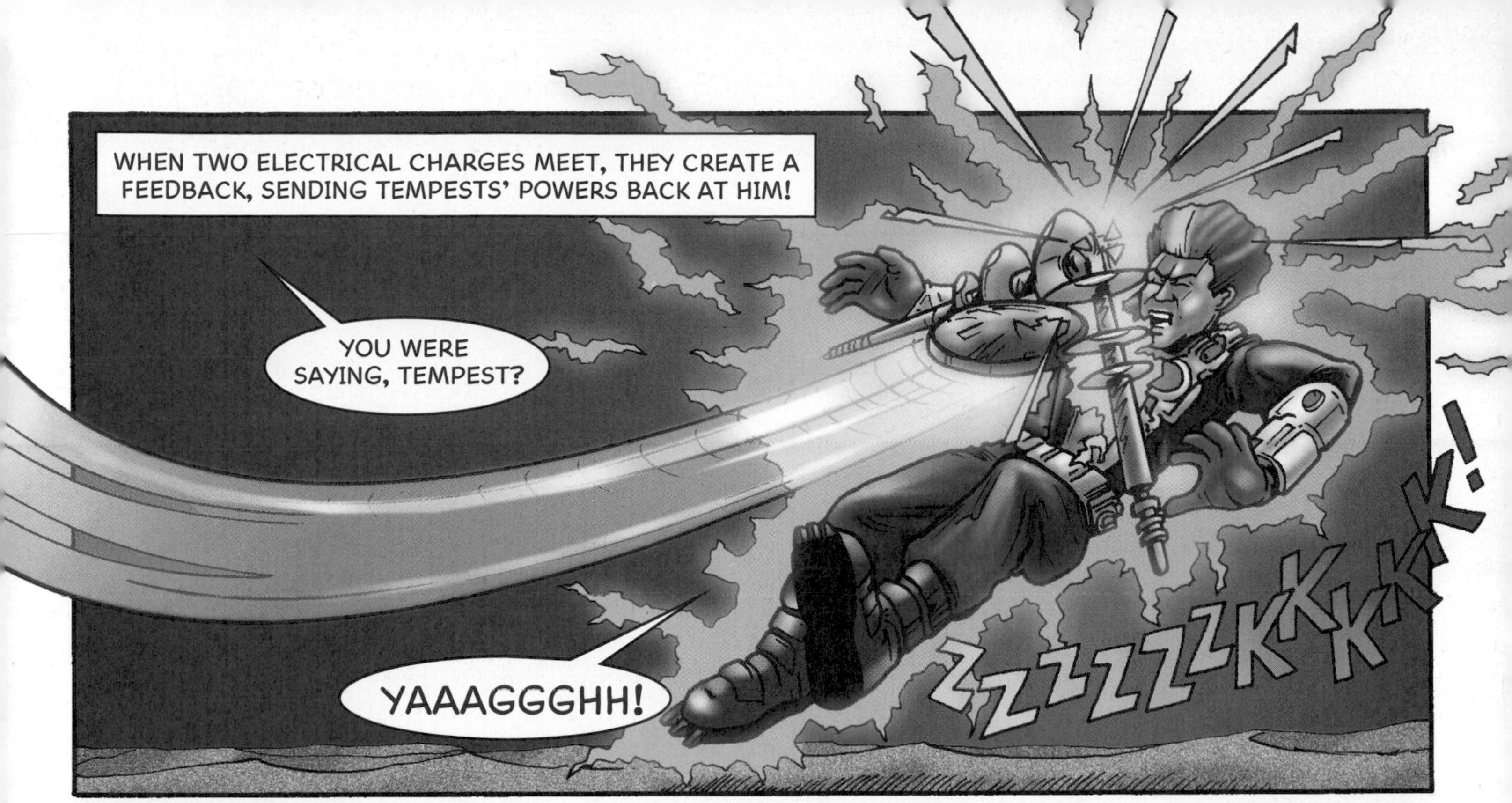

WHEN TWO ELECTRICAL CHARGES MEET, THEY CREATE A FEEDBACK, SENDING TEMPESTS' POWERS BACK AT HIM!

YOU WERE SAYING, TEMPEST?

YAAAGGGHH!

ZZZZZZZKKKKKK!

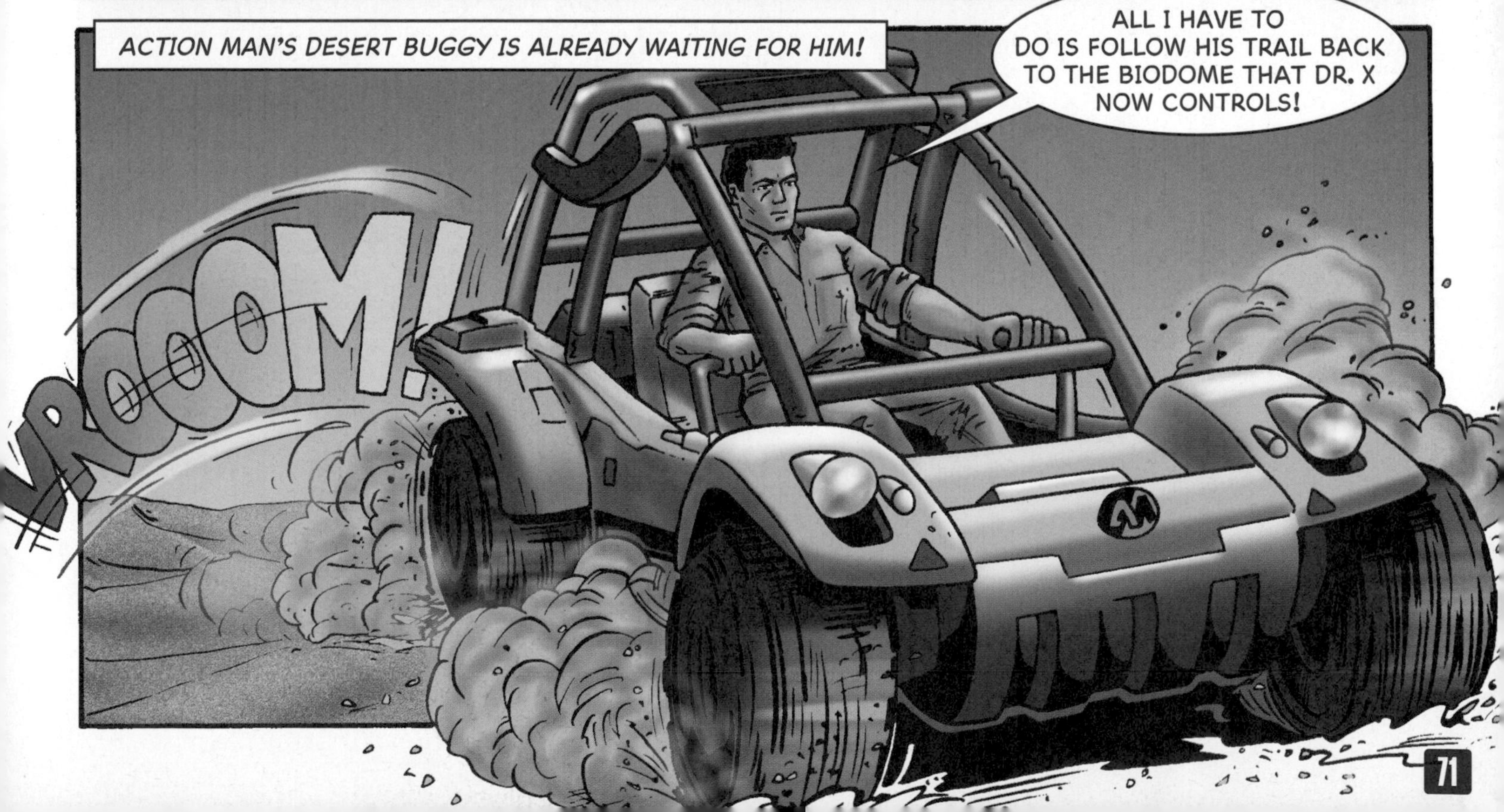

ACTION MAN'S DESERT BUGGY IS ALREADY WAITING FOR HIM!

ALL I HAVE TO DO IS FOLLOW HIS TRAIL BACK TO THE BIODOME THAT DR. X NOW CONTROLS!

VROOOM!

AM'S DESERT BUGGY ZOOMS OFF THE SAND DUNE AND INTO THE AIR.
VRROOOOOM!
WHUUMMMP!
YAAAHH!
I GUESS THAT MEANS I WIN!
CHUCKLE!

BUT A FURIOUS TEMPEST HAS ALREADY RADIOED TO DR. X FOR ASSISTANCE! AND, MOMENTS LATER...!

LOOKS LIKE THE HUNTER HAS BECOME THE HUNTED!

LET'S SEE HOW GOOD THEY ARE AT PLAYING 'FOLLOW-MY-LEADER'!

VROOOOM!

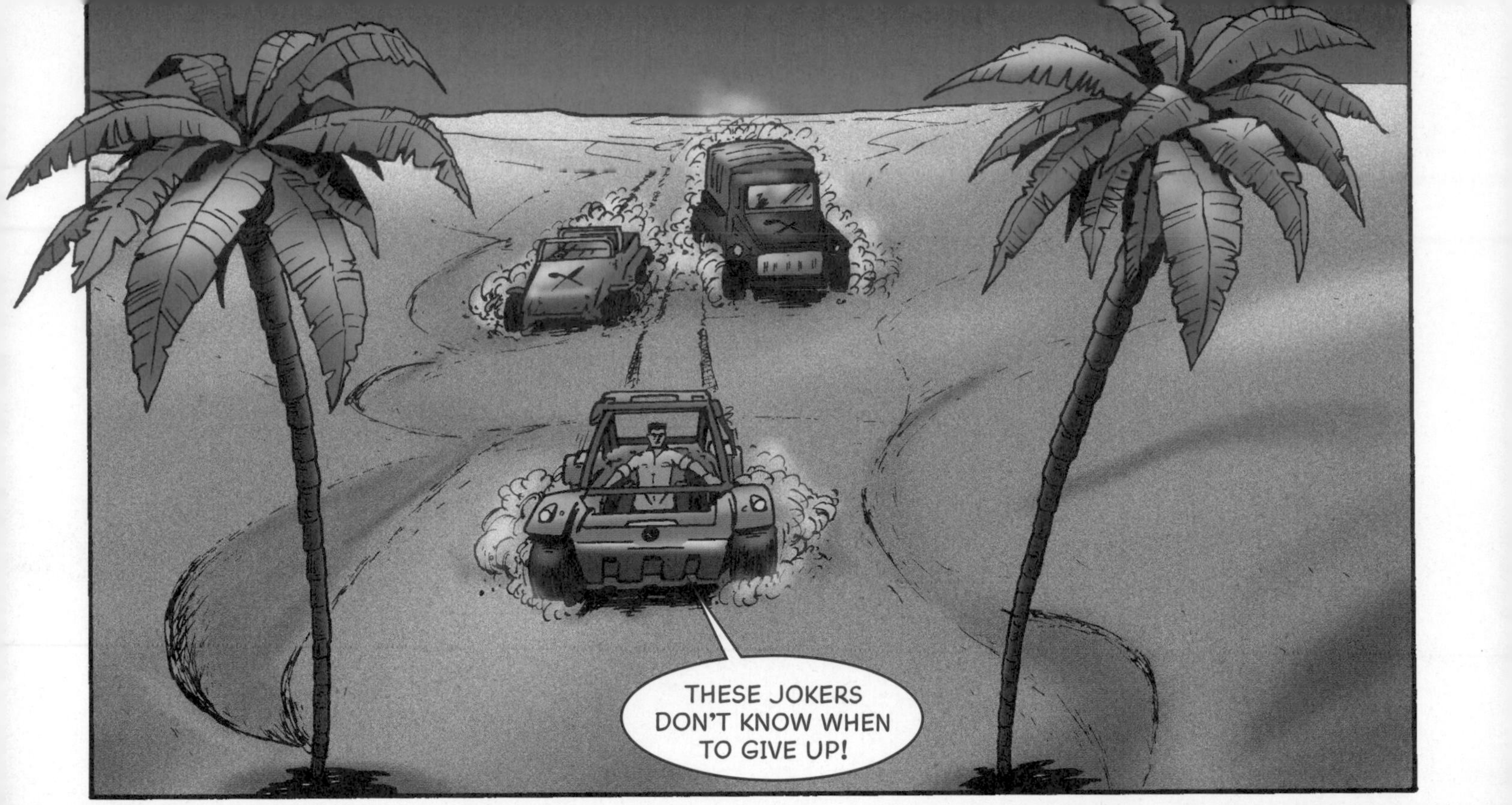

THESE JOKERS DON'T KNOW WHEN TO GIVE UP!

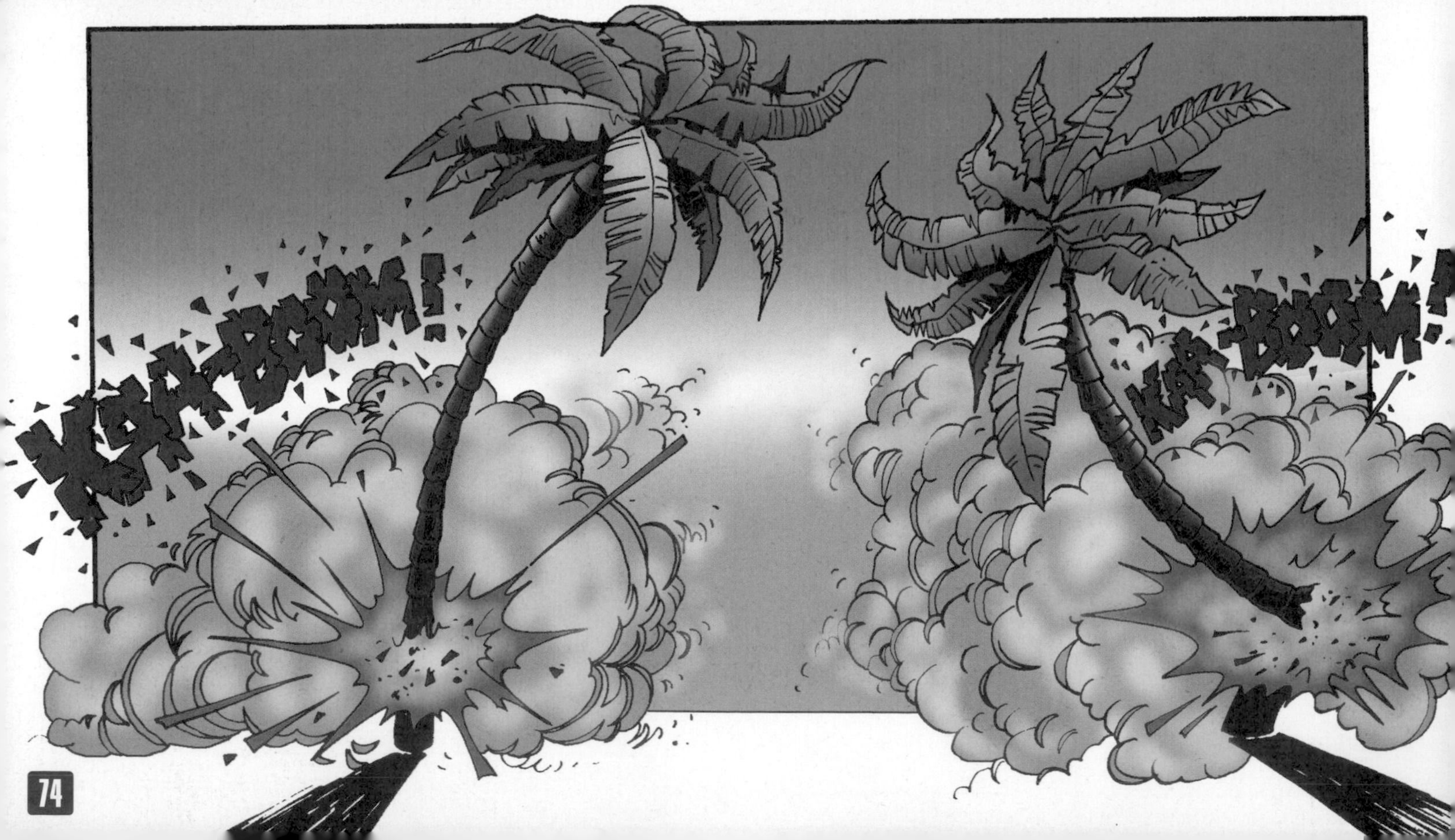

KA-BOOM!

KA-BOOM!

AAARRRGGGH!
SMASSSSH!
OUCH! THOSE GUYS WON'T BE BOTHERING ANYONE FOR AWHILE!
ZZZZKKK!
HEY, NOT BAD, ACTION MAN! YOU'D MAKE A GREAT ADDITION OF DR. X'S COUNCIL OF DOOM! PITY YOU AIN'T GONNA BE AROUND MUCH LONGER TO APPLY FOR MEMBERSHIP! HAHAAA!
ZZZZZKKK!
WHOOOFF!
KA-BOOM!

THINKING ACTION MAN DESTROYED, TEMPEST RETURNS TO THE BIODOME TO REPORT TO DR. X! BUT ACTION MAN IS FAR FROM FINISHED!
MY DESERT BUGGY IS INDESTRUCIBLE, BUT IT'S GOING NOWHERE FOR NOW!
IT'S LUCKY I HAVE MY LANDSURFER! THE WEATHER IS ALREADY STARTING TO CHANGE FOR THE WORSE, THANKS TO DR. X , BUT THE WINDS HE'S CREATING ARE WORKING IN MY FAVOUR!

AT DR. X'S SECRET BIODOME...!
ZZZZZZZZKKKKKKK!
THAT'S IT, TEMPEST! CHANNEL YOUR LIGHTNING POWERS INTO MY WEATHER CONDUCTOR, AND SOON I SHALL HARNESS THE VERY FORCES OF NATURE THEMSELVES!
WHATEVER YOU SAY, DR. X! YOU'RE THE MAN!
ZZZKK! ZZZKK!
SOON, I SHALL CONTROL THE VERY WEATHER ITSELF! COUNTRIES WILL BOW DOWN TO ME, OR PERISH WHEN I UNLEASH THE FULL FURY OF HURRICANES, TSUMANI OR DROUGHTS UPON THEM! I WILL RULE THE WORLD! HAHAHAHAHAAA!
AND WITH ACTION MAN OUTTA THE WAY, DR. X, THERE AIN'T NO ONE WHO CAN STOP YOU!
CHUCKLE!

OUTSIDE...!
DR. X'S BIODOME! I DON'T HAVE TIME FOR STEALTH! THIS PLACE HAS TO BE SHUT DOWN - FAST!
ALWAYS KNOCK BEFORE ENTERING, IT'S ONLY POLITE!
KA-BOOOM!
ACTION MAN! YOU FOOL, TEMPEST! I THOUGHT YOU SAID YOU'D DESTROYED HIM?!
BUT - BUT - ! OH, MAN! THAT GUY'S GOT MORE LIVES THAN A CAT!

BETTER PEOPLE THAN YOU HAVE TRIED AND FAILED, TEMPEST!
ZZZZKK!
GURR! THIS TIME I'LL FINISH HIM FOR GOOD!
NOW BE A GOOD KID AND BEHAVE YOURSELF! YOU COULD HURT SOMEONE WITH THOSE THINGS!
WHAAAM!
YAAAGGGHHH!
DR. X ATTACKS!
I DON'T NEED TEMPEST'S HELP TO DEFEAT YOU, ACTION MAN - I'LL DO IT MYSELF!
YOU'LL HAVE TO TRY HARDER THAN THAT, DR. X! YOUR AIM DEFINITELY NEEDS IMPROVING!

RRRRGGGH!
STAY STILL, BLAST YOU! YOU CONFOUNDED MEDDLER!
DR. X! NO! LOOK OUT! YOU'LL HIT THE WEATHER CONDUCTOR!
KRRRAAAANG!
JUST WHAT I WANTED! THANKS, DR. X! YOU'VED SAVED ME THE TROUBLE OF DESTROYING YOUR EVIL MACHINE MYSELF!
NOOOOO!
OH, NO! I'VE STARTED A CHAIN REACTION INSIDE THE WEATHER CONDUCTOR! IT'S GOING TO GO CRITICAL!

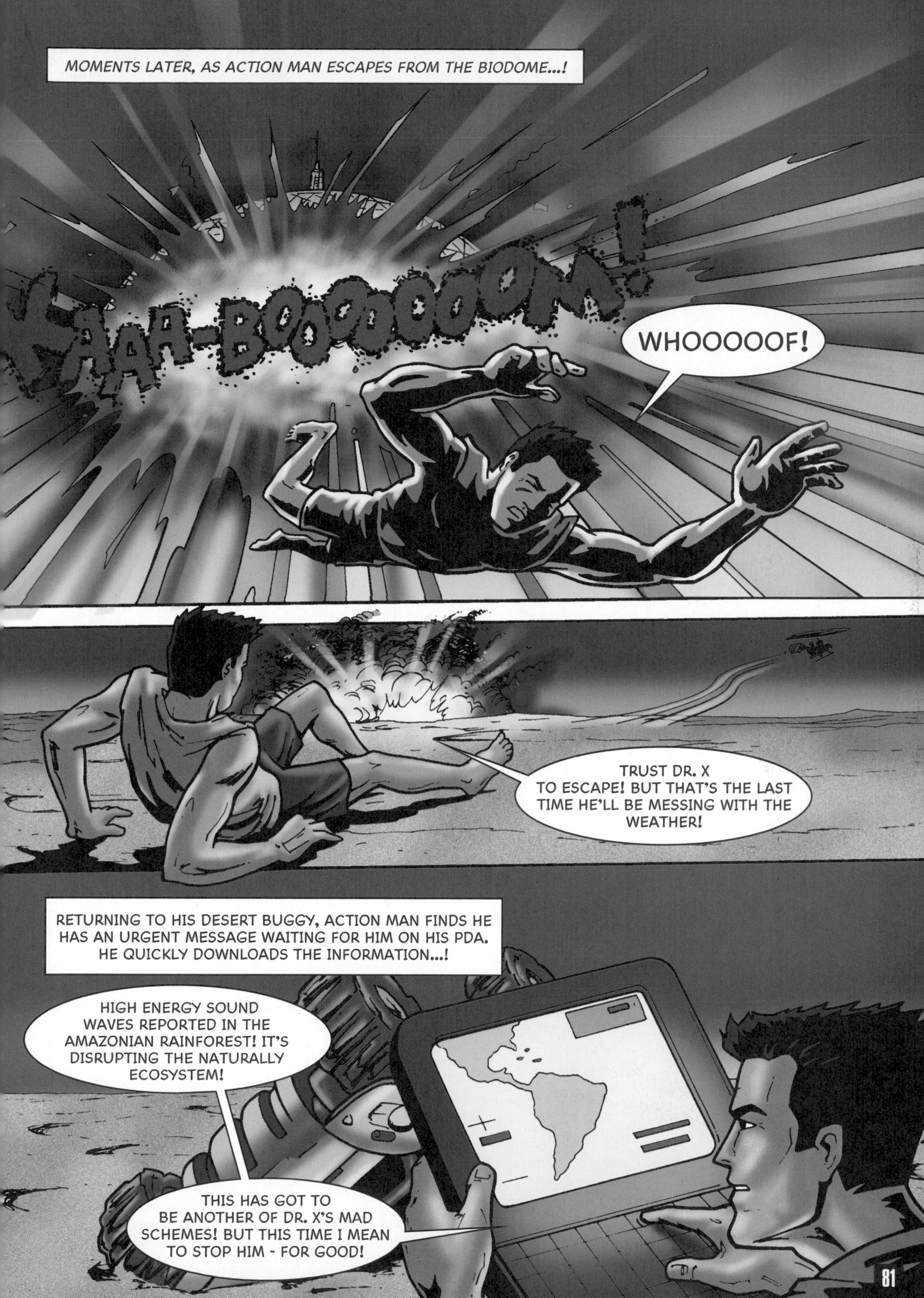
MOMENTS LATER, AS ACTION MAN ESCAPES FROM THE BIODOME...!
AAA-BOOOOOOOM!
WHOOOOOF!
TRUST DR. X TO ESCAPE! BUT THAT'S THE LAST TIME HE'LL BE MESSING WITH THE WEATHER!
RETURNING TO HIS DESERT BUGGY, ACTION MAN FINDS HE HAS AN URGENT MESSAGE WAITING FOR HIM ON HIS PDA. HE QUICKLY DOWNLOADS THE INFORMATION...!
HIGH ENERGY SOUND WAVES REPORTED IN THE AMAZONIAN RAINFOREST! IT'S DISRUPTING THE NATURALLY ECOSYSTEM!
THIS HAS GOT TO BE ANOTHER OF DR. X'S MAD SCHEMES! BUT THIS TIME I MEAN TO STOP HIM - FOR GOOD!

File Edit View Special Diagnostic Keyboard — EDA Internet

www.actionman.com/eda

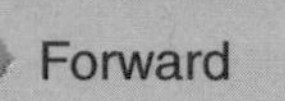 Back  Forward 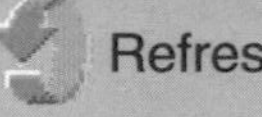 Stop 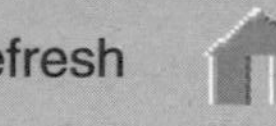 Refresh 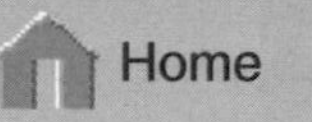 Home

Address: http://www.actionman.com/eda

Mission
Equipment
Reconnaissance
E-Mail
Encoding
Decoding
Keyboard

WORD'S UP!

Mission Data: Field Operative Training Session 2

Dr. X has been up to his old tricks again! He is hidden the names of vehicles and weapons Action Man will need to defeat him inside this word grid, plus the names of the members of the Council of Doom! Can you help Action Man find the names he`s looking for? Remember, the words can be spelt forwards, backwards or diagonally!

The words to look for are:

ARCTIC SURF BIKE MOTORBIKE EXTREME STREET LUGE

METAL DETECTOR DISC EXTREME KART EXTREME

TEMPEST STREET ROLLER ARGO DR. X AIR SURFER

ULTRA BIKE DESERT BUGGY LANDSURFER GANGRENE

Good luck!

J	A	R	C	T	I	C	S	U	R	F	B	I	K	E	E
A	D	O	E	I	O	U	F	G	H	J	E	R	T	V	M
Q	E	T	A	S	D	F	G	Z	X	C	V	S	D	W	E
L	S	C	K	J	H	G	F	E	G	R	E	Z	X	C	R
R	E	E	Z	K	Q	W	N	H	T	P	O	I	U	Y	T
E	R	T	Y	T	A	E	C	D	M	Q	S	C	F	T	X
F	T	E	Z	S	R	R	X	E	Q	A	Z	X	D	R	E
R	B	D	A	G	W	S	T	R	E	E	T	L	U	G	E
U	U	L	N	Y	G	V	D	E	T	F	C	D	E	W	K
S	G	A	A	W	S	V	G	Y	X	U	H	V	D	W	I
R	G	T	Z	E	K	I	B	A	R	T	L	U	C	F	B
I	Y	E	X	W	A	U	H	B	F	T	R	Z	S	E	R
A	E	M	E	R	T	X	E	C	S	I	D	E	X	D	O
N	H	Y	G	F	D	P	O	I	U	Y	T	R	M	Y	T
M	K	O	F	R	E	F	R	U	S	D	N	A	L	E	O
V	R	E	L	L	O	R	T	E	E	R	T	S	C	C	M

File Edit View Special Diagnostic Keyboard EDA Internet

www.actionman.com/eda

Back Forward Stop Refresh Home

Address: http://www.actionman.com/eda

ACTION MAN

Mission | Equipment | Reconnaissance | E-Mail | Encoding | Decoding | Keyboard

CRACK THE CODES!

Mission | Equipment | Reconnaissance | E-Mail | Encoding | Decoding | Keyboard

Mission Data: Field Operative Training Session 3

Field operatives must be able to crack all types of coded messages from the enemy. With the aid of the code-breaker below, see if you can break the secret messages Tempest has sent to Dr. X!

1	2	3	4	5	6	7	8	9	10	11	12	13	14	15	16	17	18	19	20	21	22	23	24	25	26
M	Q	E	Z	W	O	H	T	A	R	J	C	U	I	N	B	L	F	Y	P	D	G	X	V	K	S

Coded messages

1) 5-3 7-9-24-3 8-9-25-3-15 12-6-15-8-10-6-17 6-18 8-7-3 16-14-6-21-6-1-3!

2) 15-6 6-15-3 12-9-15 26-8-6-20 13-26 15-6-5!

3) 9-12-8-14-6-15 1-9-15 7-9-26 16-3-3-15 26-14-22-7-8-3-21 6-24-3-10 8-7-3 26-9-7-9-10-9 21-3-26-3-10-8!

4) 5-14-17-17 3-17-14-1-14-15-9-8-3 7-14-1 1-19-26-3-17-18!

5) 5-14-17-17 10-3-20-6-10-8 16-9-12-25 5-7-3-15 1-14-26-26-14-6-15 9-12-12-6-1-20-17-14-26-7-3-21!

INITIATE COMMS. MISSION STATUS MIC AM2002PDA

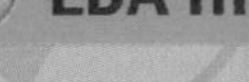

File Edit View Special Diagnostic Keyboard

EDA Internet

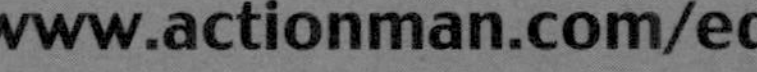

www.actionman.com/eda

Back Forward Stop Refresh Home

Address: http://www.actionman.com/eda

Mission | Equipment | Reconnaissance | E-Mail | Encoding | Decoding | Keyboard

Mission

Equipment

Reconnaissance

E-Mail

Encoding

Decoding

Keyboard

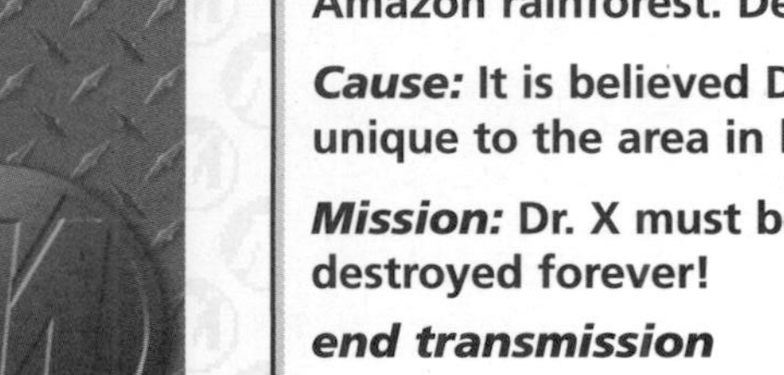

Mission Briefing: Jungle Fever

Incoming E-Mail – Secure Link Encoding

Qmwwmsr: Nyrkpi Jiziv
Qiwweki: Iqmwwmsr sj lmkl irivkc wsyrh aeziw hixigxih mr xli eqedsr vemrjsviwx. Hixempw xs jsppsa…
Geywi: Mx mw fipmizih Hv. B mw ibxvegxmrk vevi erh tvigmsyw qmrivepw yrmuyi xs xli evie mr lmw uyiwx jsv asvph hsqmrexmsr.
Qmwwmsr: Hv. B qywx
vemrjsviwx mw hiwxvs

irh xverwqmwwmsr

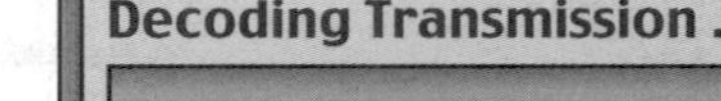

Progress

Decoding Transmission …

Mission: Jungle Fever

Message: **Emission of high energy sound waves detected in the Amazon rainforest. Details to follow …**

Cause: **It is believed Dr. X is extracting rare and precious minerals unique to the area in his quest for world domination.**

Mission: **Dr. X must be stopped before the Amazon rainforest is destroyed forever!**

end transmission

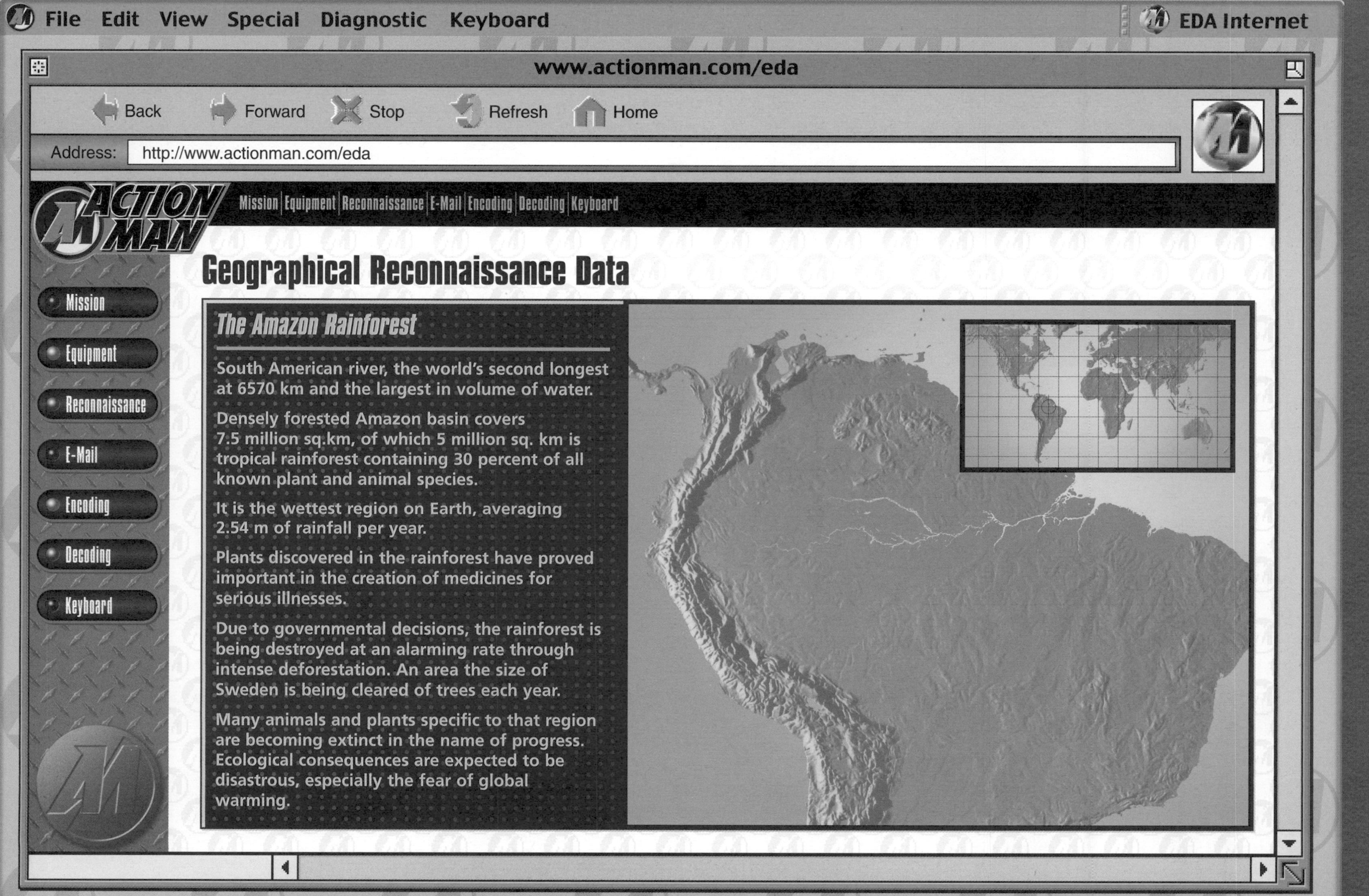
File Edit View Special Diagnostic Keyboard
EDA Internet
www.actionman.com/eda
Back Forward Stop Refresh Home
Address: http://www.actionman.com/eda
ACTION MAN
Mission | Equipment | Reconnaissance | E-Mail | Encoding | Decoding | Keyboard
Mission
Equipment
Reconnaissance
E-Mail
Encoding
Decoding
Keyboard
Geographical Reconnaissance Data
The Amazon Rainforest
South American river, the world's second longest at 6570 km and the largest in volume of water.
Densely forested Amazon basin covers 7.5 million sq.km, of which 5 million sq. km is tropical rainforest containing 30 percent of all known plant and animal species.
It is the wettest region on Earth, averaging 2.54 m of rainfall per year.
Plants discovered in the rainforest have proved important in the creation of medicines for serious illnesses.
Due to governmental decisions, the rainforest is being destroyed at an alarming rate through intense deforestation. An area the size of Sweden is being cleared of trees each year.
Many animals and plants specific to that region are becoming extinct in the name of progress. Ecological consequences are expected to be disastrous, especially the fear of global warming.
INITIATE COMMS. MISSION STATUS
MIC
AM2002PDA

File Edit View Special Diagnostic Keyboard

EDA Internet

www.actionman.com/eda

Back Forward Stop Refresh Home

Address: http://www.actionman.com/eda

Mission | Equipment | Reconnaissance | E-Mail | Encoding | Decoding | Keyboard

- Mission
- Equipment
- Reconnaissance
- E-Mail
- Encoding
- Decoding
- Keyboard

Mission Data: Equipment

Argo Jungle Explorer

Frame: Carbon fibre bonded to aluminium frame with kevlar armour

EFT: Epoxy resin fluid-filled all-terrain tyres

Top Speed: 110 mph

Navigation: GPS (Global Positioning System)

Weapons: One multipurpose Sidewinder missile. Range 1.5 km

It's a jungle out there!

Kevlar armour

All-terrain tyres

File Edit View Special Diagnostic Keyboard EDA Internet

www.actionman.com/eda

Back Forward Stop Refresh Home

Address: http://www.actionman.com/eda

ACTION MAN

Mission | Equipment | Reconnaissance | E-Mail | Encoding | Decoding | Keyboard

Mission
Equipment
Reconnaissance
E-Mail
Encoding
Decoding
Keyboard

Mission Data: Equipment

Crocodile Minisubmersible

Frame: Impact resilient polycarbonate material with kevlar armour

Navigation: GPS (Global Positioning System)

Speed: Up to speeds of approximately 60 mph

Depth: Can reach depths of 25 fathoms

Weapons: Surface-to-air Sidewinder missile

Kevlar armour

60 mph

Sidewinder

INITIATE COMMS. MISSION STATUS

MIC

AM2002PDA

ACTION MAN

JUNGLE FEVER

I DON'T KNOW WHY WE GOTTA GUARD THE ENTRANCE TO THIS RIVER, BUT WE MIGHT AS WELL ENJOY OURSELVES WHILE WE'RE DOIN' IT!
YEAH! FIRST ONE TO SKRAG THAT CROC GETS OUTTA WASHING THE DISHES FOR A WHOLE WEEK!
FZZZZK!
ZZZZK!

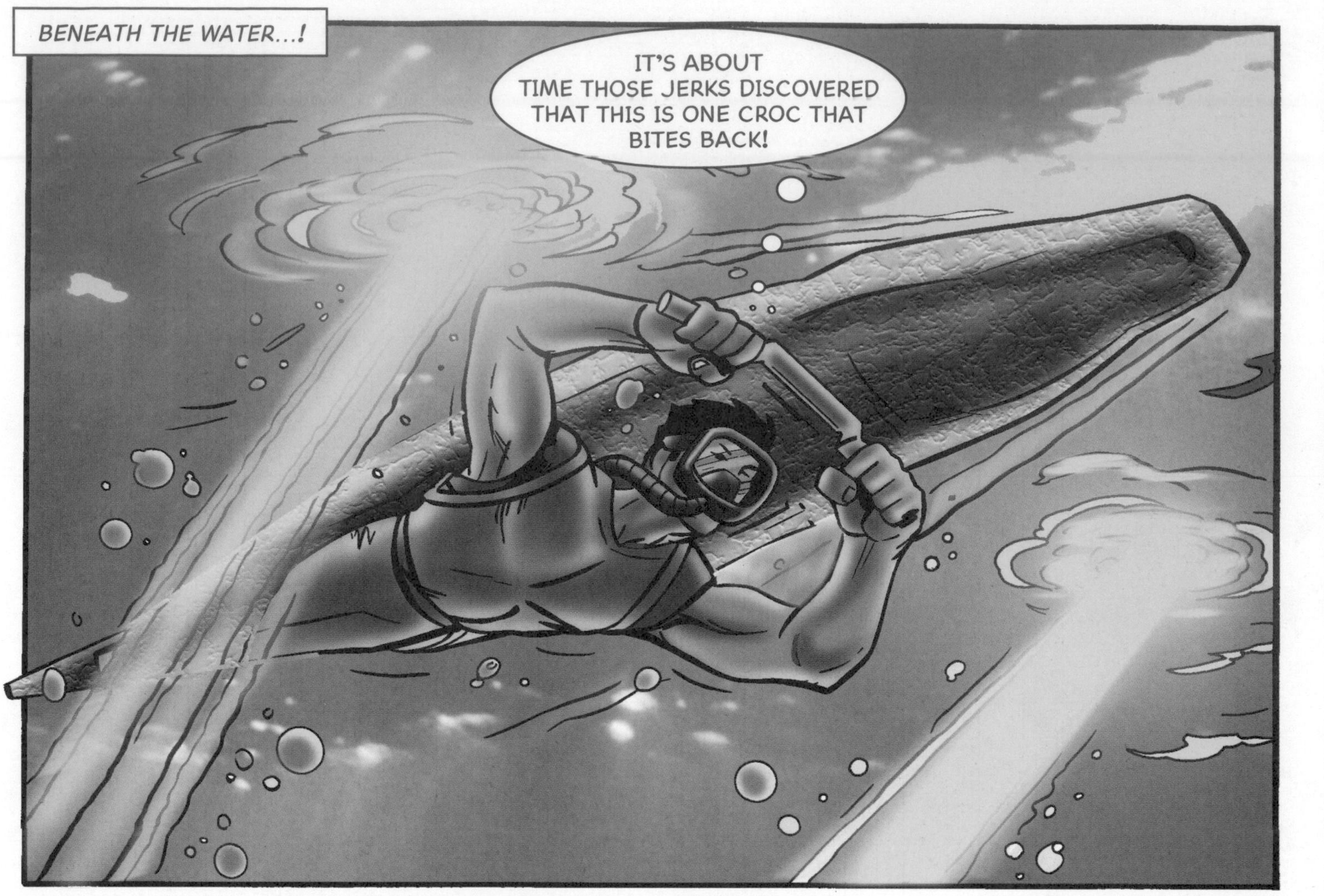

BENEATH THE WATER...!

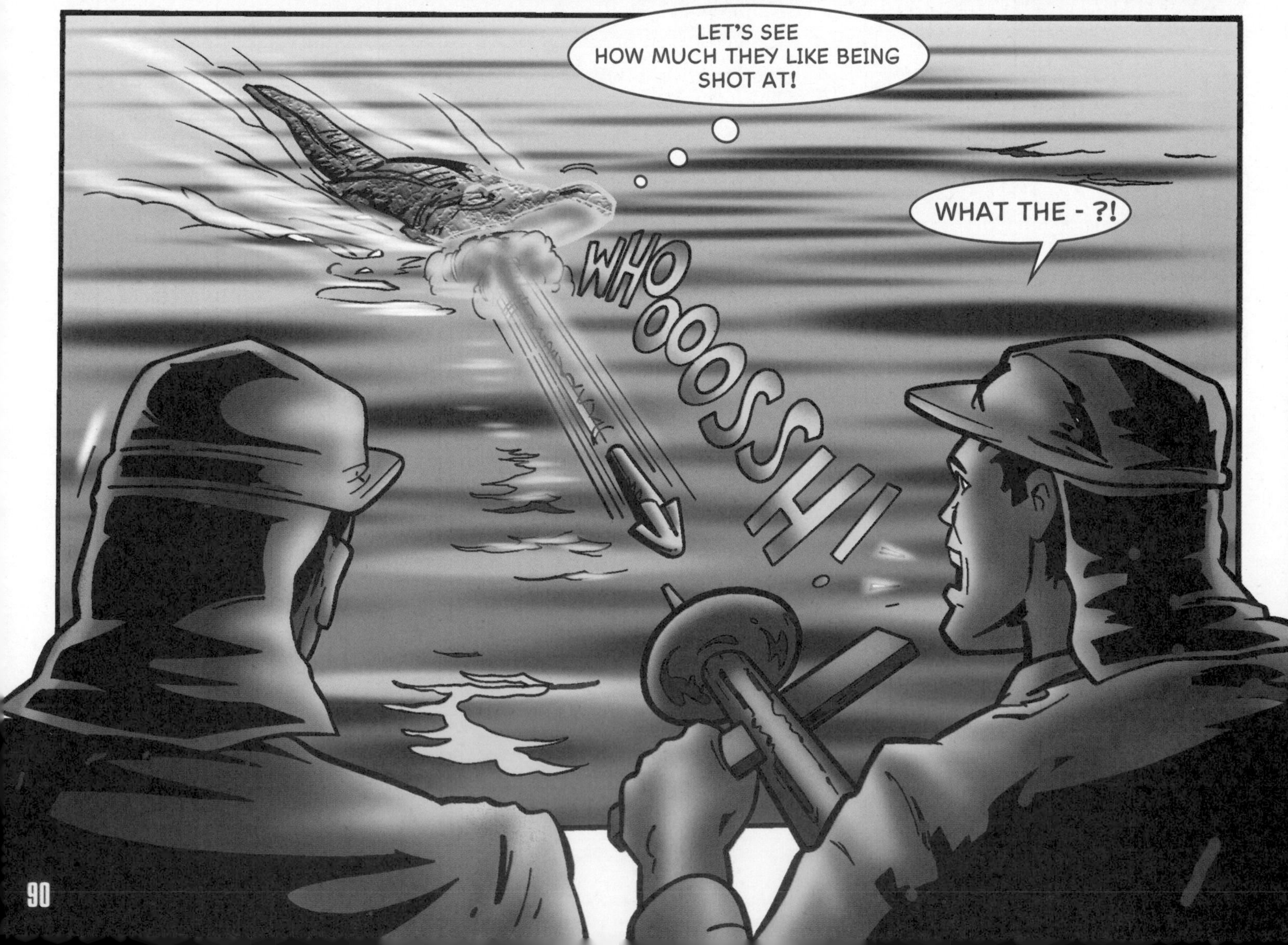

YAAAAHH!
KAA-BOOOM!
BUT ACTION MAN ISN'T OUT OF DANGER YET!
UH, OH! ONE OF DR. X'S GENETICALLY ALTERED MONSTERS! WELL, AT LEAST IT PROVES I'M ON THE RIGHT TRACK!

CRRUUNNNCH!
NOW ALL I HAVE TO DO IS SURVIVE THIS ENCOUNTER AND I CAN PAY DR. X A FRIENDLY VISIT!
THE CROCODILE TURNS TO ATTACK AGAIN!
THIS MONSTROSITY ISN'T GOING TO GIVE UP! I'VE GOT TO GET OUT OF HERE - NOW!
TOO LATE!
CHOMP!
ARRRRGGGHH!

THE CROCODILE TRIES TO PULL ACTION MAN DOWN TO THE BOTTOM OF THE DEEP RIVER BED!
IF I DON'T BREAK FREE, I'M FINISHED!
WHACCK!
GO PLAY SOMEWHERE ELSE!
REACHING INTO HIS BELT POCKET, ACTION MAN RETRIEVES A DISC EXTREME!
I DON'T WANT TO KILL THE POOR CREATURE, BUT I NEED TIME TO ESCAPE!
FSSSSSHHH!

MY DISC EXTREME IS MADE OF HIGHLY STRENGTHENED FOAM - ENOUGH TO STUN WITHOUT HURTING!
WHAAACCK!
THAT SHOULD KEEP THE CROC QUIET FOR A FEW HOURS! NOW TO TRACK DOWN DR. X!

REACHING THE RIVER BANK, ACTION MAN FINDS HIS HIDDEN ARGO AND CONSULTS HIS PDA...!
NW12, SE06, NE 24, E 02
SPACE SATELLITE TRACKING SYSTEMS HAVE PINPOINTED THE LOCATION OF THE HIGH ENERGY SOUND WAVES!
10.00.
VROOOOM!
AT TOP SPEED, MY ARGO CAN GET ME THERE IN LESS THAN TEN MINUTES!

BUT, AHEAD, PROFESSOR GANGRENE WAITS IN AMBUSH...!
HA-HA!
LET'S SEE IF ACTION MAN'S ARGO VEHICLE CAN WITHSTAND A HEAD-ON COLLISION WITH A TREE!
08.06.
NOW!
HACK!
08.01.

WHOOOSSSH!
07.58.
NO TIME TO EVADE!
BUT THEN AGAIN, I DON'T HAVE TO!
WHOOOOSSH!
07.57.
07.56.
YAAAARRRGGHH! DOESN'T ANYTHING STOP ACTION MAN?!

06.43.
GURRR!
GET HIM!
ZZZZZPP!
ZZZZZPP!
06.29.
BOOM!
BOOM!
NO WONDER GANGRENE DOESN'T HAVE ANY FRIENDS! HE NEVER PLAYS NICELY!

ACTION MAN LEADS HIS PURSUERS A MERRY CHASE!
04.36.
UH, OH! QUICKSAND! AND WITH GANGRENE RIGHT BEHIND ME, I'VE GOT NO CHOICE!
VROOOOM!
04.28.
CHUCKLE!
I'LL HAVE TO GO THROUGH IT - OR, SHOULD THAT BE, OVER IT?

PROFESSOR GANGRENE ISN'T SO LUCKY!
04.17.
GANGRENE'S SUDDENLY GOT THAT SINKING FEELING!
YAAAAHHH!
00.02.
MINUTES LATER, AND ACTION MAN REACHES DR. X'S HIDDEN LOCATION!
WHRRRRRRR
FROM THE SOUND OF THAT NOISE, I'VE COME TO THE RIGHT PLACE!

WHRRRRRRRRRRRRRRR
HAHAA!
LOOK, TEMPEST! MY MACHINE IS PENETRATING DEEP INTO THE EARTH, EXTRACTING RARE AND PRECIOUS MINERALS UNIQUE TO THE AREA! MINERALS THAT CAN BE USED TO AID MY QUEST FOR WORLD DOMINATION!
COOL, DR. X! AND IF THE AMAZON SUFFERS FOR IT, SO WHAT? IT'S ONLY A ROTTEN JUNGLE!

THE ONLY THING ROTTEN AROUND HERE, TEMPEST, IS YOU TWO!
ACTION MAN!
THE ONE THING I THOUGHT I COULD NEVER ACCUSE YOU OF WAS BEING BORING, DR. X - BUT YOUR LATEST MAD SCHEME HAS PROVED ME WRONG!
SMAAACCK!
THUDD
UGGH!
YEEOOW!

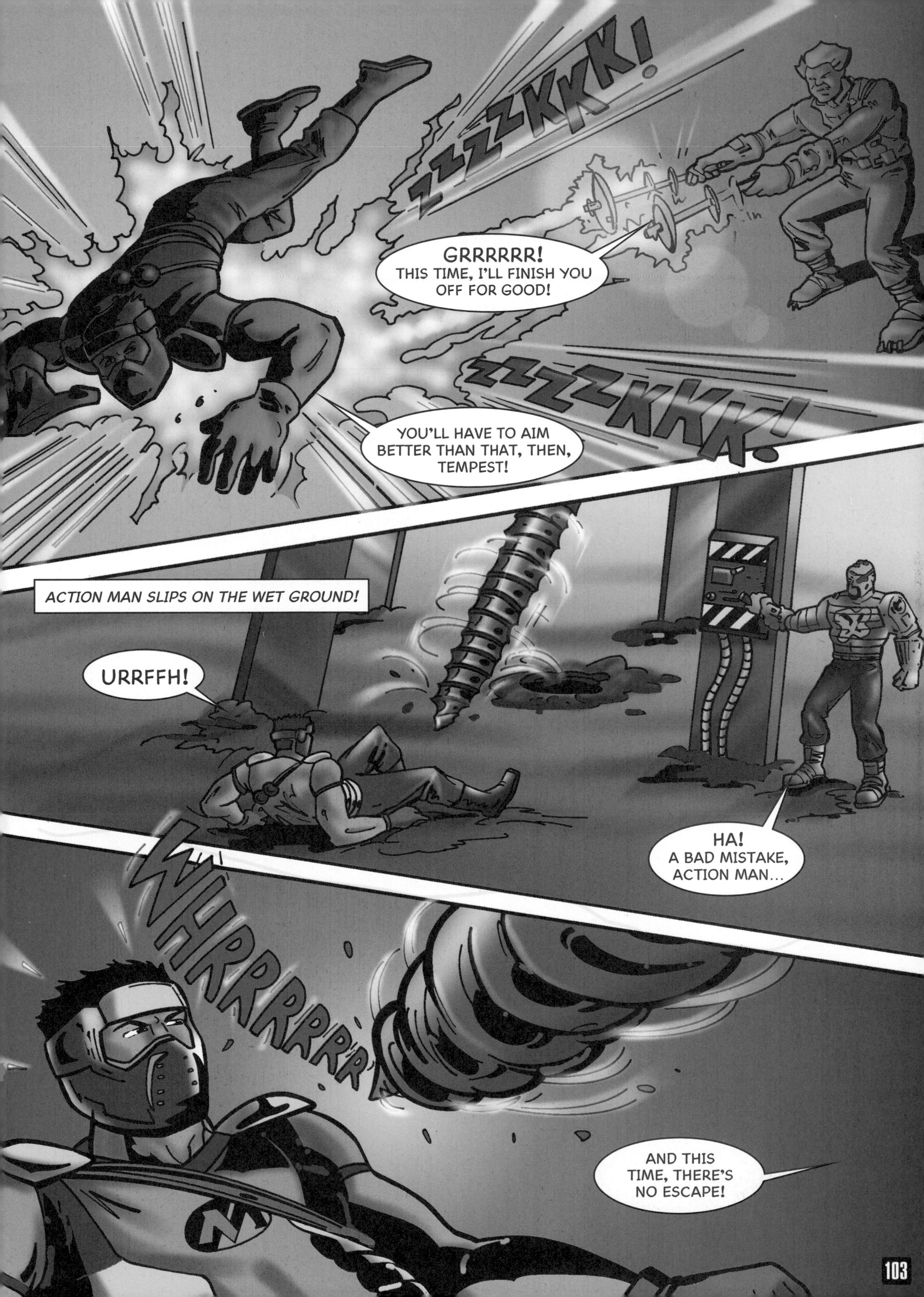
ZZZZKKK!
GRRRRRR!
THIS TIME, I'LL FINISH YOU OFF FOR GOOD!
ZZZZZKKK!
YOU'LL HAVE TO AIM BETTER THAN THAT, THEN, TEMPEST!
ACTION MAN SLIPS ON THE WET GROUND!
URRFFH!
HA!
A BAD MISTAKE, ACTION MAN...
WHRRRRRRR
AND THIS TIME, THERE'S NO ESCAPE!

ALWAYS COME PREPARED, THAT'S MY MOTTO!
WHIZZZZZZ!
KAA-BOOOM!

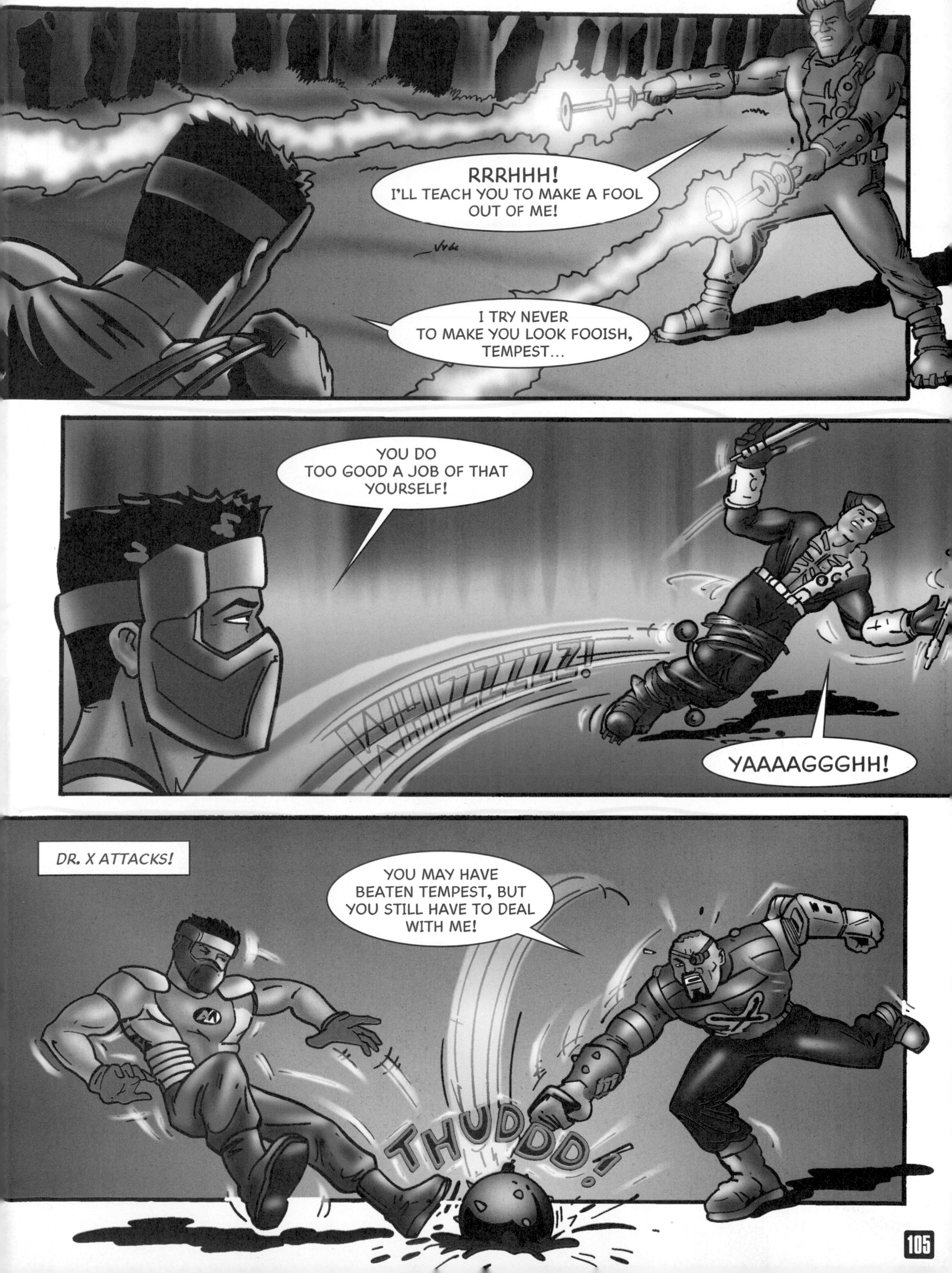

RRRHHH!
I'LL TEACH YOU TO MAKE A FOOL OUT OF ME!

I TRY NEVER TO MAKE YOU LOOK FOOISH, TEMPEST...

WHUUMMMP!
TIME FOR YOU TO COOL OFF, DR. X!
WHAAAATT?!!
SPLOOOSSSH!
BENEATH THE WATER...!
A STUPID MOVE, ACTION MAN! THIS TIME YOU DIE!
DR. X! LOOK OUT!

DR. X'S MUTATED CROCODILE ATTACKS…DR. X!

PAYBACK TIME FOR THE CROC! THAT'LL TEACH DR. X TO MESS WITH NATURE!

NOOOOOOO!

THAT COULD BE THE END OF DR. X, AT LAST - BUT I DOUBT IT! HE'LL BE BACK AGAIN TO THREATEN THE WORLD, SOME DAY… AND I'LL BE WAITING FOR HIM!

THE END

File Edit View Special Diagnostic Keyboard

EDA Internet

www.actionman.com/eda

Back Forward Stop Refresh Home

Address: http://www.actionman.com/eda

ACTION MAN

Mission | Equipment | Reconnaissance | E-Mail | Encoding | Decoding | Keyboard

Mission Data: Field Operative Training Session 4

With the defeat of Dr. X and his evil web of allies, Action Man is taking a well-earned break! And so can you! Relax from the stress of being a field operative by colouring-in this exciting scene of Action Man in the Arctic Rally car!

Mission
Equipment
Reconnaissance
E-Mail
Encoding
Decoding
Keyboard

Answers from page 83:

1) WE have taken control of the biodome!
2) No one can stop us now!
3) Action Man has been sighted over the Sahara Desert!
4) Will eliminated him myself!
5) Will report back when mission accomplished!

File Edit View Special Diagnostic Keyboard EDA Internet

www.actionman.com/eda

Back Forward Stop Refresh Home

Address: http://www.actionman.com/eda

Action Man

Mission | Equipment | Reconnaissance | E-Mail | Encoding | Decoding | Keyboard

Mission Debriefing

To help Action Man prepare for his next mission, can you extract and download the key information from the previous two missions he has just completed? Answer the questions by ticking the correct solutions.

1) In the mission Weather Warriors, what vehicle does Action Man use to reach Tokyo Airport?

A) Argo ☐
B) Ultra Bike ☐
C) Desert Buggy ☐

2) Which member of the evil team attacks Action Man when he drops down into the Sahara Desert on his Air Surfer?

A) Tempest ☐
B) Dr. X ☐
C) Gangrene ☐

3) What is Dr. X trying to do at the Biodome?

A) Create earthquakes ☐
B) Control the weather ☐
C) Destroy all plant life ☐

4) Who destroys Dr. X's Weather Conductor?

A) Action Man ☐
B) Gangrene ☐
C) Dr. X ☐

5) In the mission Jungle Fever, from what rainforest is Dr. X extracting rare and precious minerals?

A) The Brazilian Rainforest ☐
B) The Arctic Rainforest ☐
C) The Amazon Rainforest ☐

6) What happens when Action Man's Argo vehicle drives over the quicksand?

A) It gets stuck ☐
B) It gets across safely ☐
C) It breaks down ☐

7) What happens when Professor Gangrene follows Action Man across the quicksand?

A) His vehicle gets across safely ☐
B) It runs out of fuel ☐
C) It sinks ☐

8) What animal pulls Dr. X to the bottom of the Amazon river?

A) A crocodile ☐
B) A hippopotamus ☐
c) A giant sea monster ☐

Mission
Equipment
Reconnaissance
E-Mail
Encoding
Decoding
Keyboard

INITIATE COMMS. MISSION STATUS

Answers
1-B, 2-A, 3-B, 4-C, 5-C, 6-B, 7-B, 8-A

MIC

AM2002PDA